A GUIDE TO THE PSYCHO-MOTOR
DEVELOPMENT OF THE CHILD

A GUIDE TO THE PSYCHO-MOTOR DEVELOPMENT OF THE CHILD

Jacqueline Gassier
Teacher, Nursery Nurse

FOREWORD BY

Françoise Fradetal de Looze
Graduate in Psychology
Departmental Doctor for Mother and Child Welfare
Hauts-de-Seine

Churchill Livingstone ⠿
EDINBURGH LONDON MELBOURNE AND NEW YORK 1984

CHURCHILL LIVINGSTONE
Medical Division of Longman Group Limited

Distributed in the United States of America
by Churchill Livingstone Inc., 1560
Broadway, New York, N.Y. 10036, and by
associated companies, branches and
representatives throughout the world.

First edition published in French under the
title Manuel du Développement
Psychomoteur de l'Enfant
© Masson, Editeur, Paris, 1981

First edition, in English, based on the
original French edition with additional
material.
© Longman Group Limited 1984

First English edition 1984

ISBN 0 443 02969 5

British Library Cataloguing in Publication
Data
Gassier, Jacqueline
    A guide to the psycho-motor development
of the child.
    1. Motor ability in children
    I. Title   II. Manuel du développement
    psychomoteur de l'enfant. *English*
    155.4'12   BF723.M6

Library of Congress Cataloging in Publication
Data
Gassier, Jacqueline.
    A guide to the psycho-motor development
of the child.
    Translation of: Manuel du développement
psychomoteur de l'enfant.
    Includes index.
    1. Child development.   I. Title.
RJ131.G3713   1984   155.4'22   84-5819

Printed in Hong Kong
by Astros Printing Limited

Foreword

The development of a child is remarkable in its very continuity. From the newborn who comes into the world as an amorphous being, unable to perceive its surroundings, without a will of its own and incapable of thinking or providing for itself to the fully grown child, there are many stages each of which blends imperceptibly into the next. Thus it is only possible to chart a child's progress at a specific moment in time.

It is very probable that the development of the newborn is a continuation of that within his mother's womb. At birth he has only a general perception of his own body and may not even make any clear distinction between himself and his surroundings. Thus it is easy to assume that his first psychological step forward will be to differentiate between himself and the outside world and it is his relationship with his mother which enables him to make this initial, essential step. His relationship with his mother is of crucial importance. From birth the

child can hear his mother and feel her next to him and in most cases he derives great pleasure from this. The mother is the centre of the child's universe and it is she who mediates the child's perception of his surroundings.

Every young mother wonders at her child's progress, at the moment when the 'beatific smile' becomes a 'smile at other people', when the child starts to react to the sound of her voice and when he answers it by vocalising. However she still needs to know what she can expect from her child and when she can expect it. While all guides to child care provide precise dates for when a child starts to walk or cuts his first tooth, they are considerably less precise on the subject of psycho-motor development. This is why young mothers will find Jacqueline Gassier's book of invaluable assistance. The book rightly points out in the introduction that the ages given are intended only as a guide, and then gives a month by month description of the progress of the child so that

every mother can easily find the advice she seeks and allay any anxiety she may have about her child's progress.

It has been found that some student nurses and child nurses have a firm grounding in child care technique but that their knowledge of the psycho-motor development of the child is inadequate. As child nurses make up the bulk of staff in crèches and are in direct contact from morning to night with the very small child they ought to be informed about what to expect from a child so that they can act promptly should the need arise. Childminders and those who train them may also find this book of assistance. Childminders' knowledge of psycho-motor development learnt 'on the job' is sometimes scant and often outdated, based on their experience of their own children who may have grown up many years before.

Thus, it was the need for advice by parents, students, paramedical staff and childminders which led to the publication of this book. The book, written by a teacher of repute, is attractive, precise, clearly set out and easy to handle. In addition to the psycho-motor development of the child it deals with the basic problems of early childhood in an objective fashion without fighting shy of difficult areas and 'taboo' subjects.

I hope that this book finds the wide audience it deserves amongst all those who are interested in the very young child.

F. F de L.

Contents

Introduction

Every man is the sum of his childhood.
Freud

The newborn child, who is totally dependent on the outside world and reliant on a few basic reflexes, embarks on a long process of development before he can become an older child and then an adolescent. This development is marked by a series of gains which, like his very growth, are greater the younger he is.

The very term psycho-motor development implies that there is parallel development in both the following spheres:

Neuromuscular: certain groups of muscles acquire tone and these enable the child to adopt certain positions (holding head up, sitting or standing) and also to co-ordinate his motor control (use of the hands, walking).

Psychological: by stages, the child reaches greater intellectual and emotional maturity.

In the interests of clarity we intend to make a distinction between these two areas although their similarities and mutual influence will be apparent. Whereas the tiny animal comes into the world complete and totally equipped for life, the human being is born a fragile and incomplete being who must pass through many stages before he reaches total independence. The motor development of the child is not only linked

All photographs have been taken by Christian Cloquie, Versailles

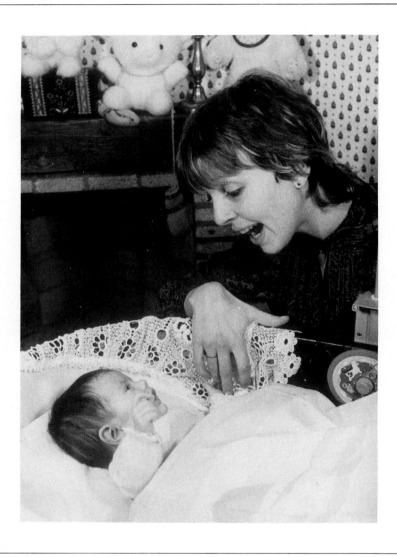

to brain development but is also dependent on a balanced diet, good living conditions, accommodation and standard of hygiene and, most especially, on a warm, caring atmosphere. Maternal love, which has been called the 'psychological growth vitamin', is absolutely essential to the well-being of the newborn. The baby's body and mind alike depend upon it.

This is why we intend to look not only at the biological process whereby the newborn gradually becomes a baby who can crawl and then walk, but also at the role of the adult in caring for the young child. Whether the influence of the parents is good or bad, what is certain is that it will mark the baby's development for life. This is why it should be studied in depth. If, at any time, I give one piece of advice rather than another, it is not because I advocate that approach alone. The advice I give is purely by means of illustration as there is no known recipe for success.

Furthermore, all the ideas contained in this book are only expressed in general terms as each child develops at his own rate and there can never be any predetermined norm. Thus comparisons should never be made between the development of brothers and sisters at the same age.

A child who grows fast may, on

the contrary, start to talk late and a child who seemed backward in babyhood may turn into a remarkably intelligent and healthy adolescent.

Therefore the ages given for the various stages of development should never be treated as grounds for concern but should help familiarize the reader with what is called 'psycho-motor development' which is just another term for 'the development of the child between the ages of 0 and 3 years'. The ages are only provided as an example and should enable readers to find their way through the text.

A child who has been helped to become a happy, fulfilled human being can only add to his parents' happiness. If the baby's early years are settled, this will always influence his future. It is not an exaggeration to say that the effort and attention given by the parents to better their understanding of their child can only be to their benefit in years to come when they themselves will be the recipients of the care and affection they have so generously lavished.

J. Gassier

Chapter 1
THE ANTE- AND POSTNATAL PERIODS

Before the birth

A woman's life changes radically when she becomes pregnant: her body undergoes major changes and she feels the presence of a new being inside her. The woman experiences moods which are typical of pregnancy: apathy or aggressiveness, irritability, anxiety, fear and difficulties in sleeping. All pregnant women experience these moods to a greater or lesser extent: they are only temporary psychological reactions to pregnancy.

For some women, pregnancy is seen as an opportunity to make good past failures and personal disappointments or even a lack of affection from their husband. The new baby is to fit into the course of somebody else's life and the very substance of this life (what the father means to the mother and what the parents feel for each other) is

Fig. 1.1 During this wait there is a whole host both of conscious, clearly avowed hopes and also those which are unconscious and unrecognised (Dr Chazaud).

sensed very early on by the child. One of the questions at the present time is whether the psychological development of the child does not depend on what he senses of his mother's feelings and the atmosphere in the family home. The role of the husband is extremely important: his relationship with his wife will influence her acceptance or rejection of the pregnancy and, by the same token, of the being who is about to be born. Even before he is born, the baby is tightly enmeshed in his parents' life together and he is bound up in a whole network of parental desires, whether these are conscious or not, and it is these which will sooner or later influence his behaviour.

It is easy for the mother to daydream about her child's future and these dreams mask a whole host of ambitions. Even at this very early stage, the parent confers on the child the role which she would have liked to have played in society. While all the daydreams a mother may have during her pregnancy will, one day, come up against reality, they do not lose their entire force and are sure to make some impression on the life of the child.

We do not intend to go into any of the wide range of unusual situations which may arise during the course of a pregnancy. Nevertheless, we should bear in mind the prime importance of those relationships which exist prior to the birth of the child as these will influence his 'future'.

Fig. 1.2 *Sophy (20) and John.* When Sophy learnt that she was pregnant she was upset by her husband's disappointment!
   John found it hard to accept the prospect of having someone else in the household, and a rather temperamental, self-centred person at that, and he feared being left out! He, who at one time had enjoyed going out to see his friends, now came home to a wife who no longer wanted to go out and who was already talking to him about his responsibilities as a father!

Birth

THE FIRST CRY

Does the baby produce its first sign of life because it is suffering? Psychoanalysts have talked at length about the trauma of birth as being a painful experience where the newborn child leaves the warmth of his mother's body to go out into a cold, harsh environment where he is all alone. They believe that, for a long time after birth, the child subconsciously misses his mother's womb and wants to return to it. This is the idea behind modern theories about natural childbirth which try to shield the newborn from the trauma of birth. However, over the past 5 years, a number of electroencephalograms have been made of babies in the process of being born and it has been discovered that the baby, who is being subjected to all kinds of physical restraints and who is being pushed in all directions, is, nine times out of ten, fast asleep!

Does this mean that we should share the view of Professor Jean Royer who sees natural childbirth as a mere fashion? Who believes that the child's cry is not one of despair but rather a 'life-giving cry' prompted by a drop in oxygen pressure? It has been proven scientifically that the child's neurological system can only start to function under the effects of 'stimuli'; light, cold and noise are all such stimuli. It is true to say that, while it does not appear essential for birth to take place with dimmed lights and soft music, it is essential for the baby to feel the warmth of a loving body next to it from the moment after birth. Sterile nurseries, where babies remain separated from their mothers for lengthy periods, do not seem to favour early exchanges of affection which are essential to the baby's development. A greater effort should be made to rectify this state of affairs.

THE MOTHER'S INITIAL FEELINGS

The mother gradually recovers from the birth over the following few days. Alone in her hospital bed she has the time to think and also to worry. She constantly asks the doctors and nurses about her baby's

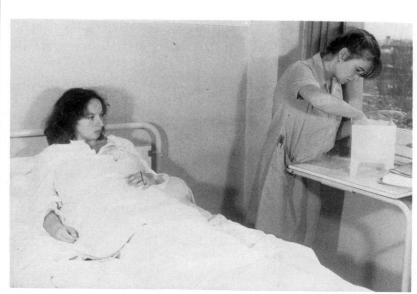

Fig. 1.3

health. She is very worried if he cries too much, does not drink enough milk and if he is not putting on enough weight. Sometimes she is even horrified at the appearance of the newborn.

Madame de Sévigné, when she saw her baby for the first time, exclaimed, 'Good Lord, isn't she ugly!' Her daughter was to become the most beautiful woman in Paris. Some mothers wonder whether they will ever be able to love their newborn, who is after all their own flesh and blood, and start to worry that they are lacking in maternal instinct. This is a very upsetting experience. In the case of a first child, the mother may worry that she will not be able to cope with this new responsibility and also with all the housework which awaits her on her return home from hospital. If the mother already has other children, she may worry about favouritism. She might say to herself, 'I would really have loved a boy and it's yet another girl. What's my husband going to say? What a disappointment!' She cannot blame the baby and does not want to question her own capacity as a mother and so she blames herself. And if, to make matters worse, lactation does not start in time or she is unable to provide sufficient milk, she treats this as a disaster and the mournful look on her face totally disconcerts her happy family when they come in to congratulate her!

Unfortunately, hospital staff do not do a great deal to reassure the young mother. They often, unwittingly, only add to her worries since often, when a mother asks for an explanation, she is fobbed off with meaningless cliches or overtechnical jargon and the communication barrier which this creates only adds to her feeling of incompetence. Paediatric nurses should do all in their power to *help* mothers over this difficult period and in order to help her as much as possible they should make every effort to understand what is going on in her mind.

The newborn

THE RELATIONSHIP BETWEEN THE MOTHER AND THE NEWBORN

It is only when one sees the newborn take his mother's breast that one can appreciate the bonds which bind him to his mother.

A primary form of language is built up between the baby and his mother, a language which does not require words but which is, in the words of Spitz, 'communication by posture'. Gestures and postures channel an exchange of happiness which is so real that it is almost touchable.

Not only contact with the mother's breast but also his bottle, bath and change of nappy contribute to this unique form of communication. These daily routines channel a two-way flow of love and affection. Winnicott[1] has studied this initial relationship between mother and child and he uses the term 'primary maternal concern' for the typical state of mind which is characteristic of the mother during the first few days after birth. Some women feel extremely sad for no conscious reason and this is perhaps due to the biological changes their bodies are going through immediately after childbirth. They tend to turn in on themselves and their child even to the extent of being unaware of the outside world. Winnicott stresses that this hypersensitive phase, where the mother is concerned obsessively with her child, is quite normal and that young mothers should not treat it as grounds for concern. It must be

Fig. 1.4 'The baby snuggles up to his mother and sometimes puts his little hand out to touch her breast while she caresses his head, gazes at him tenderly and smiles down at him.'

that nature has created this 'symbiosis' where each one needs the other and feels incomplete without the other with the purpose of giving the newborn a good psychological start to life and the mother a strong bond with her child. The baby languishes if he is

deprived of this communication. This is what happens if the mother rejects her child, if she is hostile and unyielding and if she rejects motherhood. A mother's affection is true sustenance to the child. Maria Montessori has called this the 'psychological growth vitamin' as she was extremely aware of the importance of bonds to the child's somatic development. If a child is to grow he needs to feel loved. This very special relationship can, of course, be built up with an adoptive mother, grandmother or child-minder providing that this person becomes truly attached to the child and is constantly with him.

It is extremely important for the newborn to be cared for by the same person. The baby needs certain ritual actions. The way he is held, spoken to and given the bottle add to these special moments as the child is aware of all these sensations. They become landmarks for him and aid his intellectual development. Thus, within a few weeks, the sight of his mother's face will mean 'food'.

Thus he links what he sees with a feeling of pleasure which he derives from his mother. And it should be remembered that perception and therefore knowledge will only be of value to the child if they are charged with emotion.

THE RELATIONSHIP BETWEEN THE FATHER AND THE NEWBORN

In so far as the baby, for the first month, is unable to identify the various faces which lean over the cot the father's role, at this time, may appear a secondary one. The father may feel left out and show his frustration by holding back.

As an attempt to combat this feeling, moves have been made to involve the father more in the child's birth. This is how bonds can be forged very early on, bonds which will become invaluable some months later. The role of the father is greater than he may believe and it is the fact that he loves the child's mother and helps her to enjoy being a mother which creates the happy secure environment that the child so needs.

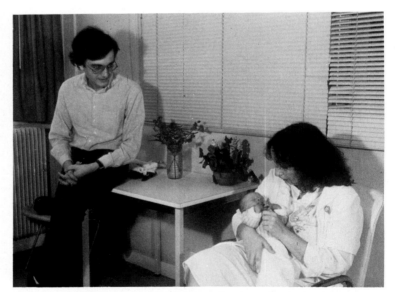

Fig. 1.5 *My life has changed.* Alan (26) has a daughter a few weeks old: 'I think that Caroline's birth has changed a great number of things. I feel closer to my wife since the birth and it has given meaning to my life. My wife spends a lot of time looking after the baby and I lend a hand (although I am rather clumsy) with all the practical work (bathing her, changing her nappy, giving her the bottle) and this helps me to get to know Caroline. We talk to her a lot and although at the moment we have to do the answering too this gives us great pleasure. We often talk about her and she has become an essential link between my wife and myself.'

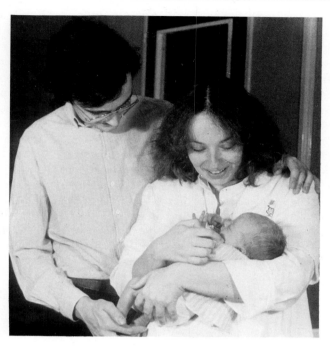

Fig. 1.6

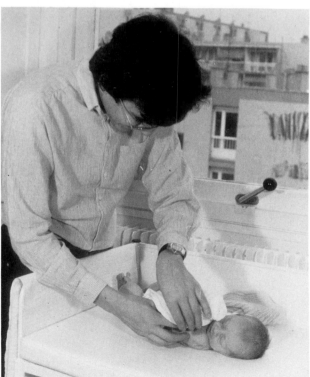

Fig. 1.7

THE NEWBORN'S CRIES

The days of a newborn a few days old are divided between long periods of sleep interspersed with the occasional short period when the baby is awake. Whether the baby is restless or not during these periods of wakefulness depends on his temperament. When the baby is asleep he gives the impression of total serenity and the only thing which ever disturbs him is a feeling of hunger when it is time for his feed.

When this moment of 'want' occurs the baby starts to scream, becomes red and contracts. He looks as if he is suffering! He feels an inner discomfort which only food can soothe.

Sometimes the infant finds himself in similar states of tension between feeds as his digestive system does not yet work perfectly. He suffers from 'mild colic'. His mother should be able to soothe him instinctively by rubbing his stomach, changing his position, singing to him, rocking his cot or by even holding him in her arms for a few minutes. Mothers are recommended to hold their babies close to their hearts (as he has lived with this very heartbeat for 9 months). This has a calming effect and he will soon fall back into an untroubled sleep. There are some parents who, over the first few months, have to deal with babies of a very nervous disposition who cry for no apparent reason and sometimes even at night! These babies apparently feel a physiological need to expend some of their energy and they must be allowed to do so without their parents falling into bad habits: holding the child in their arms for hours on end, taking the infant into their own bed, even giving him sedatives (unless on medical advice).

A mother needs a great deal of patience and love if she is to learn to soothe her newborn successfully.

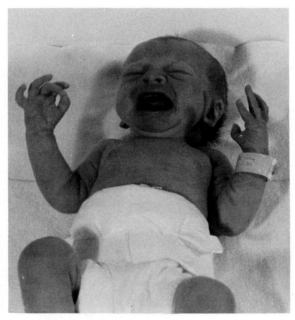

Fig. 1.8

THE PRIMITIVE REFLEXES OF THE NEWBORN

The nervous system of the newborn is not yet complete. He is a 'subcortical' being:

Scientific note

The myelinisation of the nervous system. It is known that myelinisation, that is the build up of a fatty substance (myelin) which constitutes the medullary sheath of a nerve, is the first step in the process of enabling an influx of impulses to be conducted. This development takes place by *stages*. Myelinisation reaches the bulbar centres first, then spreads to the third ventricle and finally reaches the pyramidal cells of the *cerebral cortex* (from which originate impulses to the *voluntary* muscles). At birth myelinisation has only reached subcortical centres and this is why the newborn relies on *automatic* reflexes.

His actions are therefore conditioned by what are called '*primitive*' reflexes. He reacts to stimuli by actions over which he has no control. He starts to be able to control these reflexes from birth onwards and this is what proves to the doctor that his nervous system is *normal*. The primitive reflexes remain into the second month (except in the case of the walk reflex which lasts only one week).

The primitive reflexes of the newborn

The grasp reflex (Fig. 1.9): if the palm of the hand of the newborn is stroked by an object he will close his fingers tightly round the object. This also occurs to a lesser extent with his toes.

The sucking reflex (Fig. 1.10): if the newborn's mouth is stroked he will respond by sucking rhythmically.

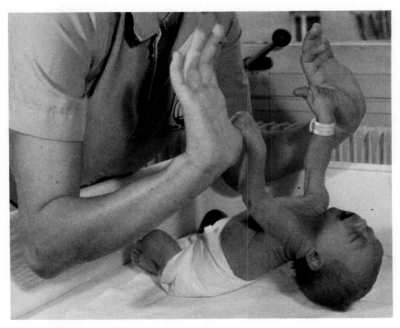

Fig. 1.9 The grasp reflex.

The standing up reflex (Fig. 1.11): if pressure is applied to the soles (in particular at the heel) of the newborn's feet he will extend his lower limbs. This reflex will disappear during the 2nd month to reappear in an active form later when the infant is able to stand up.

The walking reflex (Fig. 1.12): if the soles of the newborn's feet are stroked (if, for example, they are dragged over the surface of a table) he will move his legs as if he were walking.

The Moro reflex (Fig. 1.13): when a sudden noise is made (if someone claps their hands for example) the baby throws his arms wide apart and then closes them across his chest. This reflex can be prompted in a variety of ways and also occurs when the newborn is changed from one position to another.

The cardinal points reflex (Fig. 1.14): if the corner of the newborn's mouth is stroked he will turn his head in the appropriate direction.

Other reflexes of the newborn which do not disappear definitively:

— hiccups where the tongue and lower jaw jerk in spasms.
— *yawning* which occurs when the newborn is tired.
— *sneezing* which is a protective reflex shielding the respiratory system.
— *vomiting* which occurs when food rises up to the level of the pharynx or tongue.

There are also a great many other reflexes which are only of interest to the paediatrician who has observed the child from birth and they indicate that the baby is in a good state of health.[2]

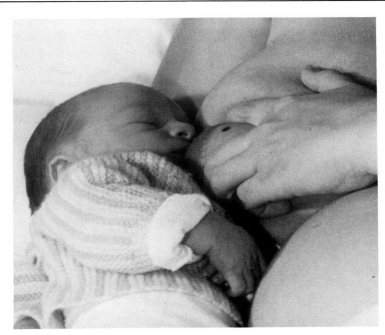

Fig. 1.10 The sucking reflex.

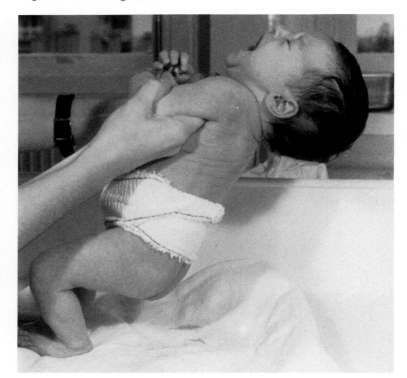

Fig. 1.11 The standing up reflex.

Fig. 1.12 The walking reflex.

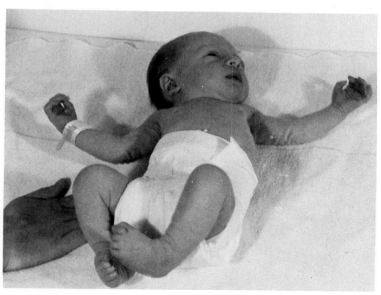

Fig. 1.13 The Moro reflex.

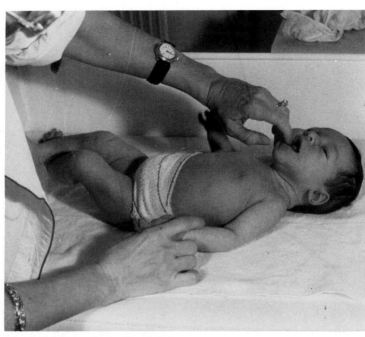

Fig. 1.14 The cardinal points reflex.

THE POSTURES OF THE NEWBORN

At birth, the limbs are characterised by *hypertonia* and the head and trunk by *hypotonia*.

Trunk

Newborn held in sitting position: the back is curved and there is no control over the vertical and lumbar muscles.

Head

Newborn held or stretched in sitting position (Fig. 1.15): the head falls forward as the neck muscles are not sufficiently strong to support it.

Limbs

Newborn held in sitting position: he can extend his lower limbs as hypo-

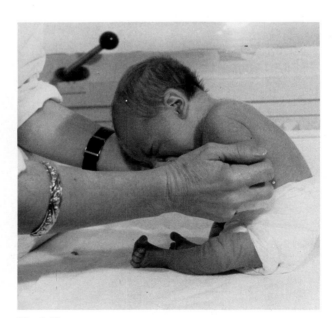

Fig. 1.15

tonia has a greater effect on the muscles used for flexion and this will decrease over the first few months.

Newborn lying on his abdomen (Fig. 1.16): he adopts the same position he used in his mother's womb (fetus position) with his upper and lower limbs flexed.

THE SENSORY DEVELOPMENT OF THE NEWBORN

Hearing

The newborn perceives sound but he does not listen to it. He is very aware of the *intensity of sound*: soft music seems to have a calming effect, he is reassured by his mother's voice whereas loud noises both excite and disturb him. The newborn cannot localise the source of sound.

Sight

During the first few days the newborn's eyes are shut (he spends most of his time asleep) and he screws up his eyes when the light changes or when he hears a sudden noise. The newborn can *focus* on a source of light but he only sees a very blurred image and he gazes at his surroundings vaguely. The newborn gazes attentively at his mother's face but until he is 3 months old he will be unable to distinguish between her real face and a stylised drawing (shown full-face and moving).

When the newborn focuses on a face he may sometimes 'squint' as he cannot yet co-ordinate his ocular muscles fully.

It has also been observed that a newborn is aware of distance: when an object is brought close to his face he moves his head back into safety!

Taste

From the time of birth the newborn has a highly developed sense of taste: he prefers sweet tastes to those which are acid, salty or bitter. If he is given a finger dipped in sugar, he will start to suck and if the finger is withdrawn, he will follow it. He will grimace if given a finger dipped in salt and does not follow the finger when withdrawn.

Touch

For the newborn touch is a form of language. Skin contact (especially with his mother's skin) and *heat* are particularly strong *stimuli*. The newborn senses through his skin his mother's vibrations and also her feelings towards him.

(One of the reasons why some children from orphanages are backward in psycho-motor development is because they are not *handled with affection*.)

Furthermore, the child is sensitive to pain but there is a long delay between stimulus and response.

Smell

The sense of smell has been studied by many writers who have arrived at a variety of conclusions. It has been proved that babies will grimace if they are subjected to a particularly strong and unpleasant odour.

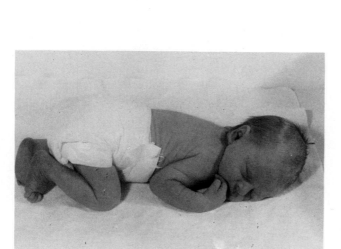

Fig. 1.16

REFERENCES

1 Winnicott D W 1960 Through paediatrics to psychoanalysis. Hogarth Press, London
2 Compare Koupernik 1976 Développement neuropsychique du nourisson. P.U.F., Paris

A GUIDE TO THE CHILD'S DEVELOPMENT

The descriptions which follow provide some insight into the process of motor and intellectual development of the child between the ages of 1 month and 3 years.

They focus, in particular, on the way in which, from one month to the next, one kind of behaviour leads on to another. The ages mentioned are merely the statistical averages of the results of the research carried out by Gesell and Illingworth. Each stage of development is dependent on a number of factors which need not always occur at the same rate. For example, the stages of development relating to the use of the hands and walking depend on the individual child and one may take longer to develop than the other.

It should be borne in mind that this guide gives a *general* picture within which a number of variations are possible since every child has his own personality and rate of growth.

Chapter 2
PSYCHO-MOTOR DEVELOPMENT FROM 1 MONTH TO 3 YEARS

THE FIRST MONTH

General appearance

What can the 4- to 6-week-old baby now do that the newborn could not?

A close observation of his behaviour will show that he has made enormous progress: he has increased muscle tone, his muscles give him greater support and so he is not as weak and fragile as he was at birth. He can breathe more regularly, suck and swallow better and therefore he regurgitates less. He also has fewer apparent nervous symptoms such as hiccups, twitching, trembling and sneezing.

Nonetheless, the baby's movements are still jerky as his leg and arm movements are still controlled by *primitive reflexes*.

Postures

A newborn lying on his abdomen:
   Trunk: still slack, no muscle tone.
   Head: slack, turned to one side, although he may occasionally raise his chin (when held in a sitting position his head will fall backwards unless supported by an adult — Fig. 2.1).

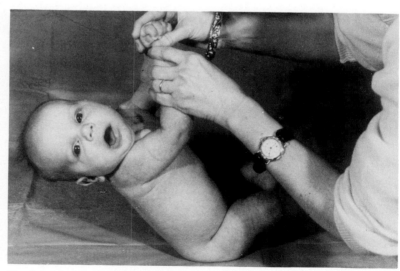

Fig. 2.1 1 month: the baby's head is still slack and falls backwards.

Lower limbs: during the first 2 weeks the baby remains in the foetus position: from the 4th week onwards his knees are no longer drawn up against his abdomen and he *intermittently extends* his hips(*crawling movement — Fig. 2.2*).

Upper limbs: his elbows are still bent and he keeps his fists clenched (the grasp reflex) but he is finding it easier to open them from time to time (Fig. 2.3)

Lying on his back: he can flex both upper and lower limbs.

The use of the hands

The *grasp reflex* is still present. If a finger is slipped into the palm of the baby's hand he will grip it tightly.

Sight

Lying on his back the newborn will look at anything which is within his field of vision (if, for example, a rattle is shaken in front of him): his

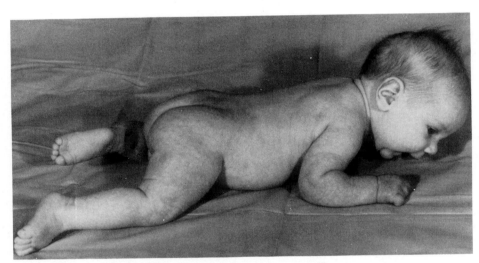

Fig. 2.2 During the 1st month the baby makes intermittent crawling movements.

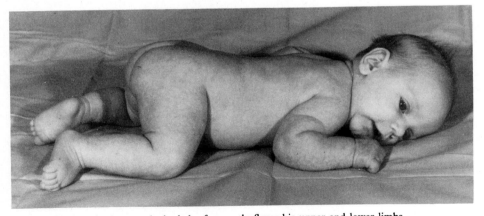

Fig. 2.3 During the 1st month the baby frequently flexes his upper and lower limbs.

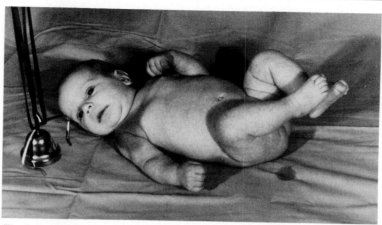

Fig. 2.4 1 month: the baby can focus on a large object and follow it through an arc of 90°.

eyes are *expressionless*. From the 4th week the baby can focus on an object and follow it through an arc of up to 90° (Fig. 2.4). He is attracted by light and will look towards an open window or a sunlit white wall (although too much light or colour excites him).

His mother's *face* provides an excellent visual stimulus, he smiles at her when he is being fed and watches her intently when she talks to him. However, Spitz has shown that it is not the *face* as we see it which causes the newborn to smile but rather a moving *shape* (or *Gestalt*). A baby will also respond with a smile to a cardboard image (a stylised picture of a face made up of two to six black dots). The baby does not respond when shown the card in profile.

Hearing

The baby reacts to loud noises and is soothed by music (except before his feed when he is hungry!). He has a very good sense of hearing but cannot yet localise sound.

Language

The baby makes guttural sounds to communicate his emotions. He also communicates by crying. He stops crying when his mother picks him up or talks to him: contact between mother and child during the feed is of crucial importance. From this age onwards the baby should be talked to often: he may not understand the words but he will be aware of the affection his mother's words convey and this is the best stimulus he can have.

Mary Ann (4 weeks old)

Mary Ann is in her cot. She has just gone back to sleep after a long cry due, no doubt, to a wet nappy. After changing her nappy, her mother rocked her for a while, sang her a few lullabies and Mary Ann soon calmed down. She first looked over in the direction of the bedroom window which was letting in a ray of sunlight and then she went off to sleep. Asleep, she is the very picture of peace, lying on her back with her little fists clenched and from time to time an angelic smile lights up her face to her mother's delight. 'If only she could stay like that until the next feed!'

Social development

For the first 3 weeks only the breast or the bottle calms the newborn's cries. However, once the baby is 1 month old, he will stop crying when his mother comes over to him or talks gently to him. He becomes increasingly *receptive* to the sound of the human voice, to light and to songs; he enjoys a nice warm bath and he likes to be comfortably wrapped up. This is why, if he is crying because he has a wet nappy he will stop as soon as it is changed. This kind of cry is quite different from the cry of hunger. 'At this age the type of cry differs according to the nature of the discomfort.'[1] The parent needs to be able to find out why the baby is crying to be able to comfort him.

The baby responds well to all these efforts to improve his 'wellbeing'. He may even give a flicker of a smile and while it is not always clear who the smile is intended for it can only signify some feeling inner wellbeing. At the age of 4 weeks the baby is only awake for short periods.

He spends the best part of the day asleep which allows his body to build up strength.

He is often awakened by crying (whether he is hungry or not). Gesell[1] has said that in the late afternoon (around 5 to 6 p.m.) there is a period of 'presocial' behaviour and that this opportunity should be grasped for bathing the child; 'his eyes are wide open and his body is less active'.

He is not yet ready to get to know his mother as he cannot yet distinguish between *himself* and *what is not himself*. He can now focus his eyes better and when he is attracted by some optical stimulus (for example, a ray of sunlight on a wall) he will look at it intently. This does not mean that he can perceive what he is looking at in detail as his nervous system is not yet sufficiently mature to enable him to do so.

A 2-month-old baby should not be exposed to too many *stimuli* as these tend to excite him. The parent should shield him from bright light, bright colours and loud noises. Television sets and record players should be turned down, shouting and loud conversations should be avoided and small brothers and sisters should not be allowed to create a racket near him. Specialists have observed that there is a change in the rhythm of breathing when even slight sounds are made. Parents should try to provide a warm but fairly tranquil family atmosphere so that the baby can enjoy the peace he needs.

2 MONTHS (8 WEEKS)

Motor development

Whilst motor control is still undeveloped and the baby gives involuntary starts, the primitive reflexes begin to disappear. The baby can now move his entire body, and his arms and legs are becoming more supple.

Postures

Trunk and head

Lying on his abdomen: His head is generally turned to one side and he can raise it from time to time: his face is raised to an angle of 45° from the plane of the bed (Fig. 2.5).

Held in a sitting position:
— His back has straightened slightly although it is still slack.
— He can hold his head up for a few moments but it wobbles (Fig. 2.6).
Stretched backwards from a sitting position: his head falls back (Fig. 2.7).
Limbs: a reduction in hypertonicity.
Lying on his abdomen:
— Lower limbs: his abdomen lies flat and his hips are extended.
— Upper limbs: his elbows are still bent but are more supple.
Lying on his back: he can flex his muscles more easily because he is more supple (Fig. 2.8).

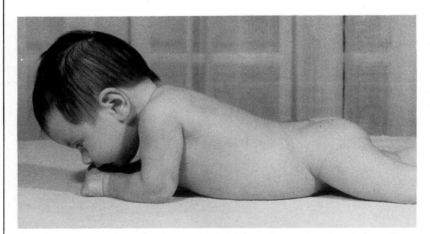

Fig. 2.5 2 months: the baby can raise his head from time to time (to 45° from the plane of the bed).

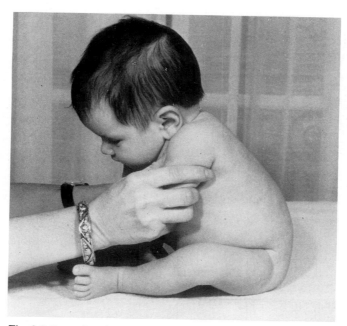

Fig. 2.6 2 months: the baby's back is not yet firm and his head wobbles.

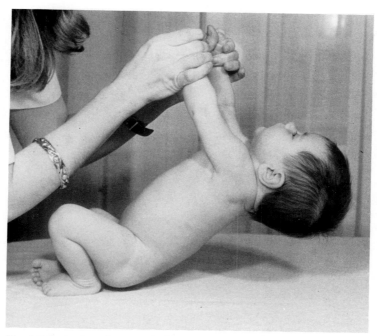

Fig. 2.7 2 months: when stretched backwards from a sitting position the baby's head falls back.

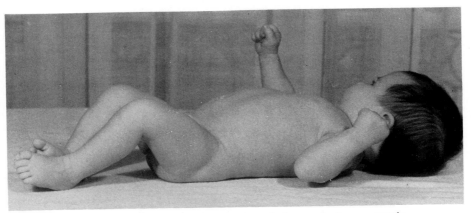

Fig. 2.8 2 months: the baby can flex his limbs more easily because he is more supple.

The use of the hands

His hands are more frequently open. The grasp reflex is becoming less apparent.

Sight

He can perceive, focus and adjust to distance. He can follow a large object or a person moving around him. When he is lying on his back he can follow an object through 180° (from one side of the bed to the other). His attention is attracted for longer periods by sharply defined, moving or brightly coloured objects as well as light. When he is shown several objects he will focus on only one. Babies of this age prefer to watch moving people than moving objects.

Hearing

— He can localise sound
— He likes to listen to a variety of sounds.

Language

The baby starts to vocalise; he makes cooing noises which are vowel sounds using the mouth alone. He cannot yet nasalise (this is due to a close neuro-psychological link with the sucking reflex).

The baby makes ah, uh, eh usually when he is happy and these sounds, surprisingly enough, are the same for babies throughout the world.

Most of the time, however, the baby communicates by crying.

Virginia (8 weeks old)

Virginia is crying in her cot after a long sleep. Her mother leans over to say hello and Virginia smiles at her as if to tell her how happy she is. Her mother tries to amuse her before her feed by talking to her about her own little world: her bedroom. She says, 'Look at the pretty blue, green and red mobile up there on the ceiling. It's turning, just for you.' Virginia looks at what her mother is pointing at, coos with delight, gets excited and vocalises. Then her mother rattles some bells at the foot of her cot. Virginia stops moving and opens her eyes wide with delight. 'How she would just love to catch hold of them, if only she could!' But her little hand is quite happy to grip tightly to her mother's finger. Virginia tosses a little and then starts to cry again. Her mother wheels her cot into the kitchen. When they get there, Virginia calms down and lies quietly, trying to *follow* her mother's movements and apparently listening to familiar sounds.

Social development

At the age of 2 months the baby has become much more alert and aware of what is going on around him. The actions he mimics are much more expressive; he can stop for a moment to have a look around; he is more active, more *alert*; he vocalises when he is happy and he becomes quiet the instant the side of the cot is let down to give him his bottle or simply to talk to him.

The baby needs to be surrounded by a warm, loving atmosphere; this is what he craves and is vital to his wellbeing. At 2 months he will give the long-awaited *first smile*. This marks a milestone in his development. He smiles at familiar faces (father, brother, sister) and especially at his mother. This is her reward. The mother should realise, however, that each baby has his own, individual personality; some are given to smiling less than others. There is no reason to start blaming oneself for not having given the baby enough loving care. Nevertheless, it has been shown that the baby can be encouraged to smile by gestures with the head, little 'conversations' with him and smiling back at him. At this age, once the baby's basic needs have been attended to, he is able to play an active role in the family. He stays alert for longer if people communicate with him. He seems to seek stimuli and his environment can and should provide these: Dr White of U.S.A. has been a leading figure in carrying out experiments at his creche into the impact of the environment on the baby. He observed that *white* surroundings impeded the infant's progress whilst the greater stimulus and excitement of *brightly coloured* surroundings encouraged progress. So he had the walls painted in colours, put up pretty pictures and used attractive sheets with pictures of animals, flowers, etc. He also asked for cots with bars so that the infant could look out at his colourful *environment*.

It did not take Dr White long to come up with convincing results: the children did take an interest in their little world and showed an advance of 8 to 9 weeks in their psycho-motor development. Gesell claims that 'it is just as important for a child to see bright colours as it is for him to have food in his stomach. It is even possible to stop a baby from crying by showing him a brightly coloured cushion!'

Toys

Children should be allowed to live in a world of colour. Parents should not hesitate, once their baby is 2 months old, to decorate his room, hang mobiles from the ceiling, attach bead frames to his bed or show him a simple, small, brightly coloured *rattle*. It is a wonderful experience for a mother to study and guide the development of her baby and his increasing awareness of what is going on around him. She understands her baby's every demand and can meet his needs better than any other thanks to what the writer Bernanos has called, 'the intelligence of the heart'.

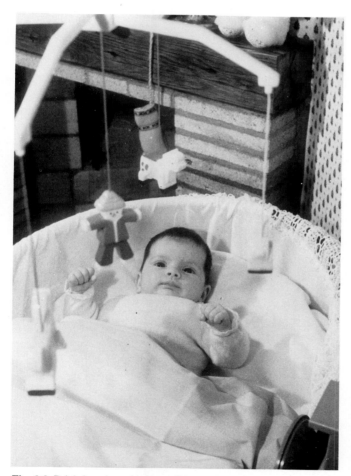

Fig. 2.9 Brightly coloured surroundings and mobiles stimulate the baby's progress.

3 MONTHS (12 WEEKS)

Motor development

The brain has developed further and the primitive reflexes have disappeared. During the transition period between the time when muscles are controlled by reflex action and the time when they come under the voluntary control of the baby himself, the infant will appear to have less motor control. He will move his arms and legs less than previously.

Postures

Lying on his abdomen: he can easily raise his head for some minutes and his head is raised to a 45-60° angle to the plane of the bed.

In a sitting position: his back and the nape of his neck are now firm (Fig. 2.10). The newborn can hold his head up.

Limbs

Lying on his abdomen:
— *Lower limbs:* the abdomen of the infant lies flat against the bed.
— *Upper limbs:* the infant supports himself on his forearms when he raises his head. He can co-ordinate arm and leg movements on both sides.

Lying on his back: he can both flex and extend his legs (Fig. 2.11).

The use of the hands

The grasp reflex has disappeared. The infant covets objects with his eyes but is not yet able to pick them up by himself (Fig. 2.12). When an adult 'touches' his hand with a rattle, he opens his hand, then closes it and manages to hold the object for a number of seconds: this is due to *involuntary grasping* (Fig. 2.13) also known as *grasping on contact.*★

★This type of grasping, where sight plays no role, is referred to by psychologists as a 'tactile motor reaction'.

Sight

He can turn his head right round to follow a moving object. The baby enjoys the movement as much as the actual sight of the object. He starts to take an interest in his body starting with his hands: this is the age for '*staring at his hands*'. He will also concentrate on nearby objects, he might stare intently at a toy that is set in front of him. He can also look at something further away if it interests him and he can look from one object to another.

Hearing

He turns his head towards the source of the sound and is perfectly capable of localising sound. He can distinguish between *sounds* and *voices* and is particularly interested in the human voice.

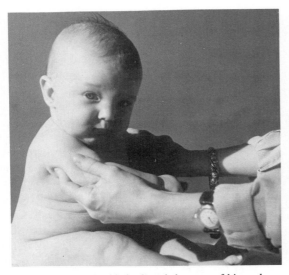

Fig. 2.10 3 months: his back and the nape of his neck are now firm.

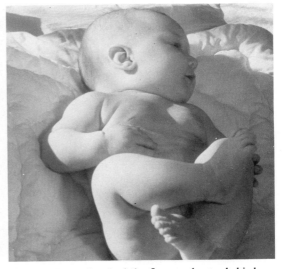

Fig. 2.11 3 months: the baby flexes and extends his legs.

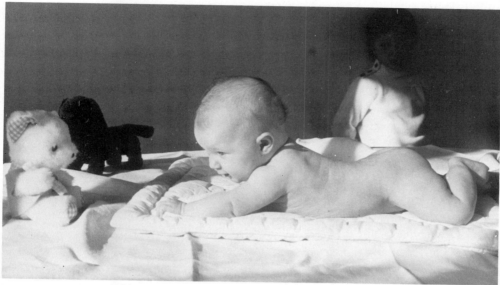

Fig. 2.12 3 months: the baby cannot yet grasp objects by himself.

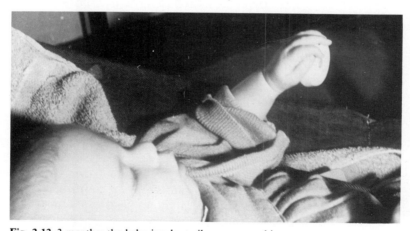

Fig. 2.13 3 months: the baby involuntarily grasps an object.

Language

He squeals with anger or delight depending on his mood. He cries a great deal less than previous months and he *communicates* a great deal when people take an interest in him. He progresses from 'vowel sounds' to 'consonant sounds'; he starts to pronounce k, g and r and then adds p and b which he finds a little more difficult. He repeats *combinations of syllables*. At this age he *gurgles* (makes prolonged vocalisations). *For example*:

Ah . . . roo
G. . . roo
K . . . roo
Ah . . . groo

He enjoys varying his phonic repertoire, gurgling and cooing and he enjoys the vibrations he feels in his lips.

John (12 weeks old)

John has just woken up quietly and he smiles as he gazes at his hands playing in front of him. His eye goes from one to the other as if in rapture over some new discovery.

He babbles, coos and gurgles with delight, spends a long period on his own amusing himself in this way and then starts whimpering for his mother. After such a long sleep he would so like to see her again. Mother comes in and says hello as she picks him up and starts playing bumpety-bump with him. John squeals with delight! Suddenly a door bangs and the baby looks round in the right direction. Of course, it's Patrick, home from school. John smiles at him and leans forward to indicate that he wants to go to him. So Mother puts the baby into his baby-seat and leaves the two brothers together to talk. They have so much to tell each other!

Social development

The baby is much more open to the outside world: through his 'talking' (prolonged vocalisations) and his mimicry, which helps him to express his feelings, he is now much closer to the adult. He now cries rarely or not at all during the daytime. At this age he may, of course, cry to say that he is hungry but the sight of his bottle being prepared or his mother coming over is enough to calm him.

At 3 months the baby is very reliant on *body language* to make himself understood; when he cries, whether in delight or distress, he wriggles his whole body and moves his arms and legs. He may stiffen when his mother wants to put him to bed, lean forward if he wants to be lifted out of his high chair, or lean his whole body towards any object he covets; he is a much more independent little being who is able to make his intentions felt; he has his own way of whining when he wants his mother, of protesting if he is changed from one activity to another too abruptly or if he is interrupted when engaged on some activity on his own.

3 months is the ideal time for him to start to *socialise*: he wants to see faces and he thrives on company. To help him to take part in family life he should be put in a baby-seat; this little chair is ideal because it allows the baby to sit up (the baby likes it because it holds his head up) while giving support to his back which is still weak.

The baby's sleeping habits are now well-established; he has a more regular routine and can sleep for some hours in the morning and afternoon. However, he may have difficulty in sleeping through 8 to 10 hours at night. At the beginning parents should be careful to avoid answering the infant's every call as this will quickly condition him. The mother should try, no matter how difficult she may find it, to let the baby find his own methods of getting back to sleep. On the contrary, any calls made during the day should be answered immediately. The baby must be able to make the connection between signal and response. It is a very sad thing to see babies in children's homes who are left to cry for hours without anyone coming to see to them.

It is very important for babies of this age to have a routine in their daily lives, in the people they see and the care they receive. Babies like to be handled in the same way and at the same times and they enjoy the same games repeated over and over again. All these routines enable the child to become better acquainted with his environment while at the same time providing that essential feeling of *security*. As Dr Anna Freud said, 'The world must be predictable for them.'[2]

At 3 months the child should start to be weaned: he can be given vegetables and fruit and these can be spoonfed. Mealtimes should be an affectionate time for the child; the mother should be happy and relaxed, talk to him, show him the patterns on his plate, how the spoon is used, the colour of the vegetables. If the infant does not want to eat he should not be forced on any account. And if the child gobbles up his first meals the parent should try not to make 'too much out of it': there is no point in playing games with him as the child should regard mealtimes as *'pleasant in themselves'*.

Psychologists have observed a major increase in the activity of babies at 3 months in comparison with previous months. The baby can now play for periods of up to 35–40 minutes.

He suddenly takes an interest in his hands; he watches them as he brings them together and then opens them wide again, he looks from one to the other, he puts them in his mouth and sucks them for long periods. Oral contact allows him to discover a source of sensory stimulation. This is how the 'eyes-mouth' process initiates his discovery of his own body.[1] The infant also starts to discover objects; he holds them in his hands for long periods, looks at them and puts them in his mouth. Thus his ability to carry out actions is linked to visual and oral pleasure. The more he repeats these actions, the more he will link 'cause and effect' and the better he will remember it. All these little actions provide the infant with a fascinating game and if the parent wants to aid the child's development there are certain toys which are particularly suitable for this age group. They should be simple in shape, flexible, have rounded edges and be appealing to the eye and the ear. The parent should therefore choose toys which are brightly coloured and which move.

Toys

Musical rattles (hand-held or attachable), brightly coloured *counting frames*, *mobiles* (the infant can now look at each figurine on the mobile in detail, his field of vision is widening as is his curiosity), *little plastic animals* and *musical boxes* are most suitable at this age; however it should not be forgotten that the best stimulus the infant can have is his mother talking and listening to him, cuddling him, encouraging him and picking him up. 'The stimulus provided by the mother is vital to the child's future.'[2]

4 MONTHS (16 WEEKS)

Postures

Trunk and head

Lying on his abdomen: the infant can raise his thorax and head until the plane of his face makes a 90°

angle with the plane of the bed (Fig. 2.14).

Sitting: the infant holds his head up well, his back and the nape of the neck are firm although the lumbar region is still weak and needs to be supported (Fig. 2.15).

Stretched from sitting position: his head follows the rest of his body.

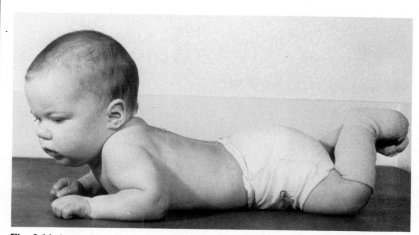

Fig. 2.14 4 months: with his forearms bent the infant can raise his thorax and head to 90°.

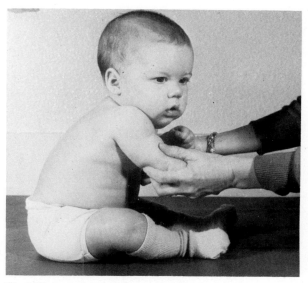

Fig. 2.15 4 months: the infant can hold his head up but his back is still weak.

Limbs

Lying on his abdomen: his legs are extended, the baby *swims:* he can extend and flex all his limbs.

Lying on his back: he tries to put one foot on the opposite knee.

His pelvis lies completely flat on the bed and the soles of his feet also lie flat on the bed.

He tries to roll from one side to the other or from his side on to his back.

The use of the hands

He has much better command over his hands and his movements are more varied. He does not mind which hand he uses. He can bring his hands together when he plays which enables him to play with a rattle for longer; he looks at it,

rattles it but frequently *drops* it. He will try to grasp at an object (for example, a cube or a hand) which is put in front of him (Fig. 2.16). He takes everything to his mouth.

Sight

His visual capacity is close to that of an adult. He can adjust to distance and perceive the smallest detail. Thus his interest is held for longer and he can spend quite long periods just looking at an object.

Hearing

The baby can hear very well now; he can identify familiar sounds and accurately localise their source, turning his head in the right direction.

Language

The quality of his voice gradually improves and his intonation becomes much more varied. *The infant gurgles,* he makes long 'conversations' by combining 'vowel sounds and consonant sounds'. He especially likes oo: this will lead to:

oo ah
ah oo   (oo + vowel)
ah ooah
and then to:
p oo
b oo   (oo + consonant)
m oo

followed by 1, and then shortly afterwards by t, d, n, etc.

'A delay in the production of these consonants might denote a weakness of the child's lips. That is why children should be introduced to more solid food from the 4th–5th

Fig. 2.16 4 months: the infant starts to grasp at objects which attract his interest.

month onwards to stimulate their muscles and to promote better pronunciation.'[3] It should not be forgotten that language is also a means to communicate affection and a baby who knows he is loved will have no problems with language. At this age the child will vocalise a lot if talked to. He gives little cries, coos, gurgles, chuckles or laughs out loud. He can now vocalise his sheer delight at being alive for periods of 20 to 30 minutes at a stretch!

Natasha (4 months old)

Natasha is sitting in her little high chair; she has just had her rest and her mother has brought her into the kitchen so that she can feel part of the family.

Natasha is wide awake and draws attention to herself by lots of vocalisation. From her intonation it is obvious that she is addressing everyone around her. Will she manage to win over her small brother? He seems quite unperturbed and is doing his homework in the dining room, but Natasha wants to play. There's that cube on the ground in the corner of the room and it's been intriguing her. It's definitely what she wants and she madly waves her arms for some kind adult to go and fetch it for her but to no avail! Everybody is busy. So she will just have to think of a way to make up for it on her own and thankfully nature has seen to it that she has two perfect toys, her hands. She can have fun just looking at them, touching them, folding them across her chest. Finally, while she is watching her mother doing the cooking she starts to suck her fingers with the utmost absorption.

Social development

The baby's body is firmer: he has better *muscle tone* and he is *stronger*. He now has to be kept under close supervision as he might easily fall out of his cot or chair if his mother does not keep an eye on him. Since he no longer really enjoys lying down, and he is now able to hold up his head, it is best to put him into a baby-seat. This will give him the support he needs and enable him to play a role in family life as this is a time when socialisation is at a peak. The baby is interested in everything and can stare for long periods at familiar faces, objects in a room, people moving around him (Fig. 2.17). During the day he stays awake for increasingly longer periods and at night he can sleep for 12 hours at a stretch. He often wakes without crying. If he is calm he can talk to himself for up to 30 minutes while waiting for his feed. At four months the baby can be patient (even when he is hungry) because he knows the familiar sounds which tell him that the bottle is on the way. He can *anticipate* events. He now knows his mother very well and gives her a special smile when she comes to look after him. At this age he begins to co-ordinate his visual capabilities and can see almost as well as an adult which means that he can make out every little detail of his universe.

Nonetheless, his discovery of the world starts with himself and the baby stares at his hands for long

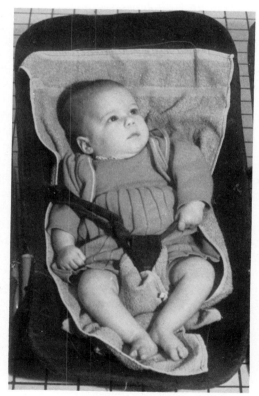

Fig. 2.17 4 months: the infant is very alert and gazes for long periods at people moving around him.

periods. He crosses them, claps them, touches them, 'his hands manipulate his hands, he touches and is touched' says Gesell, and he takes them to his mouth. *Sucking* is an extremely important activity and he can spend hours sucking his hands and his fingers, exploring his face. This is what he does with every object; he looks at it, feels it all over and then puts it in his mouth.

This is a continuation of '*hand-mouth*' process which started at 3 months (see p 24) and which marks a crucial period for the acquisition of knowledge (perception of space, shape, distance, weight); he starts to become aware of his own movements and gradually to differentiate between himself and everything else. When he is handed an object he will look back and forth from the object to the hand which is holding it and will thus become better able to discriminate between the hand and the object.

Toys

These are extremely valuable aids as the child is very keen to explore things with his hands. The sight of toys alone is enough to stimulate him and his need to hold them, touch them and grasp at them is very strong. At this age he does not need a wide variety of toys as he will spend long periods playing the same games over and over again with each of them and spend a long time sucking them.

The choice of toys will therefore vary little from what he has had previously: musical *rattles*, *mobiles*, *counting-frames*, *rubber animals*. He could also be given a *crossbar* (which will stimulate him to grasp) and some brightly coloured plastic cubes. He will still derive the greatest

enjoyment out of games played with his family. At this age a very active baby will only be prepared to interrupt a game he is playing on his own to try and get his mother and family to join in. He adores taking a small building block from his tiny brother and he will be even happier if his brother is patient enough to pick it up for him each time he drops it.

If his play is suddenly interrupted because it is time for his feed he will be only too willing to voice his disapproval by screaming and wriggling his whole body.

As we have already said, a 4-month-old child has his own, individual personality and he enjoys playing with adults. When he is picked up he peers at the face of the person who is holding him. He tries to make out what the person wants and will make definite attempts to communicate.

Once he trusts those around him he will make long 'conversations' with a wide variety of intonation. In fact, a child of this age is extremely sociable and takes easily to new faces (this will not last long) and delights in anything new. The parent should not hesitate, therefore, to take him out on walks, to visit friends or even away on a trip, without, of course, overdoing the number of trips or changes of scene because the baby may become unsettled and nervous. At the same time, the parent should ensure that the infant has a regular daily routine as this is vital for his development.

5 MONTHS (20 WEEKS)

Postures

Trunk and head

Lying on his abdomen: the infant's body is now very firm and he can raise his head and a major part of his trunk off the couch by supporting himself on his forearms.

The infant is extremely active: he stretches his arms and legs out wide and sometimes even tries to lift them off the couch in a swimming movement (Fig. 2.18) supporting his weight on his thorax (he flails his limbs in the air like an *aeroplane*!).

He tries to roll over from his abdomen on to his back (Fig. 2.19).

Stretched from sitting position: he now actively helps with this movement by raising his head and bending his legs so as to push his body forward (Fig. 2.20).

Limbs

If he is held upright he can support a considerable part of his own weight. He makes a lot of pedalling movements with his legs.

The use of the hands

He now starts to *reach voluntarily* for objects: the infant is capable of reaching voluntarily for objects which are set in front of him (Fig. 2.21). When he is offered an object he stretches out his hand towards it to grasp it.★ This kind of grasping is done with the *palm* and is a *general*,

★This type of grasping, which links sight and touch, is referred to by psychologists as a 'visual-tactile reaction'.

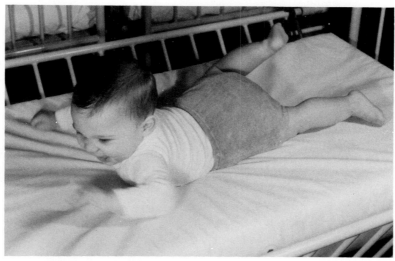

Fig. 2.18 5 months: he can extend and flex all his limbs.

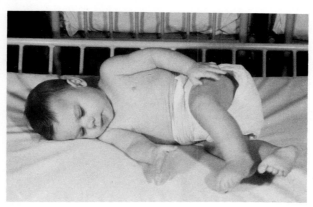

Fig. 2.19 5 months: he tries to roll from his stomach on to his back.

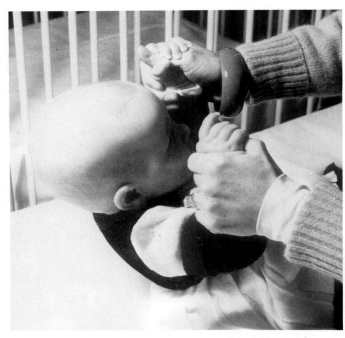

Fig. 2.20 5 months: the child actively helps when he is changed from one position to another

Fig. 2.21 5 months: he starts to grasp voluntarily for objects with his whole hand.

imprecise movement: the infant takes hold of a large object with the palm and the last three fingers of the hand.

He takes all objects to his mouth.

He uses both hands to touch and feel the edge of a table or any other form of support within his reach.

Sight

The infant has extremely accurate vision from the 4th month onwards (see p. 28).

Language

Language in the 5th month is broadly similar to that of a 4-month-old baby. The child still delights in vocalising. He watches people's mouths with great interest and listens attentively to the different intonations and sounds he hears around him. His main interest is the human voice and he will turn his head and look to see who is talking. Parents should therefore try and talk as much as possible about what they are doing so that the child can make unconscious connections between 'words and actions' as these will be of use to him some months later. For example, when parents are getting their child ready in the morning, instead of dressing him in silence, they should try and create some warmth by talking the baby through the operation ('Give Mummy your little foot now') and by varying their intonation (the infant will react to this). He will reply by babbling or by expressing himself through his actions. This will help him to associate language with feelings of affection and wellbeing. A whole new learning process needs to be set in motion; the infant will be very receptive to this and if he is encour-

aged and feels that the language he makes is accepted by his family he will make much more progress than a child whose vocalisation is ignored. Babies need not only to be given the tools to communicate but also the desire to do so.

Neil (5 months old)

It is 6 o'clock in the morning. After having sucked his hands for a short while, Neil decides to waken the entire household and his yells are far from welcome at that hour in the morning. Dad gets up, gives him his bottle to see if that will calm him down but when it comes to lying down again Neil twists and turns and makes it perfectly obvious that he has no intention of going back to bed. His father is unaware that Neil is no longer particularly interested in his own little bed . . . it's become somewhat constricted at his current rate of progress and he would much prefer his Dad's big bed or his little chair so that he can see and hear what is going on . . . and touch. But his Dad does not seem to understand that and all he does is rather unwillingly to put the baby on to his tummy in his little playpen. Neil protests loudly about having to lie on his tummy but finally decides to make the best of it. He gets up on to his forearms, raises his head and starts to explore, 'Oh, what a pretty red cube!'. He picks it up with his whole hand, explores it, takes it to his mouth and then drops it . . . so he starts crying again.

Social development

5 months is the age when the infant starts to *reach voluntarily* for objects and this marks a milestone in his development as he starts to learn to use his hands. When he decides, of his own free will, to pick up a toy he begins to sense that it is not part of him, that it is something separate. If he drops it he will lean over to look at where he has dropped it. But he lives for the moment and if it disappears from view he does not look for it. He believes that objects either exist or they do not!

This ability to stretch out a hand to grasp something teaches the

infant the relationship of 'cause and effect' and this he will remember. He will gradually be able to recall his actions and the effects they have had. This new ability leads the infant to become obsessed with objects. He wants to touch everything in sight and the upright position is infinitely more exciting for picking up objects, touching them and banging them on the table.

It should not, however, be forgotten that the infant has made progress in other areas: he has better motor control and his muscles now enable him to do new things: he can make swimming movements with his feet and legs, he tries to roll over from his abdomen to his back and he can raise his head and his trunk some distance from the plane of the bed. He can therefore be encouraged to do this by being laid on his stomach.

The infant is unlikely to appreciate this new initiative as he still prefers the sitting position (with support). He will no doubt protest loudly but soon come to appreciate the advantages of this new position. It is a good idea to put him in a *playpen:* if the floor is flat and something soft is placed on it, the child will be able to indulge in a variety of new exercises. If his mother helps and encourages him he will enjoy playing at being a 'barrel' and rolling from his tummy on to his back, and picking up a cube while lying down. These little games provide him with an excellent form of gymnastics for strengthening his back muscles. There is a further advantage to placing him on his stomach (according to I. Lézine): 'the child can move about easily which increases his scope for exploration and his hands are kept busy by being on the ground and are less likely to be "sucked", an activity which is particularly frequent at this age.'

Also, while the infant is lying on his stomach, a *mirror* can be placed in front of him: he will be very intrigued at his own reflection and will smile at it without recognizing himself (it is not until the 7th-8th month that the child will distinguish his own image from that of other people and will try to touch it). Between the ages of 5 and 9 to 10 months there is a period where the child is acquiring so many new abilities that he may sleep for shorter periods.

Indeed, it has been observed that difficulties start when the child learns to do certain activities such as 'voluntary grasping' and 'walking on all fours'. The child gets very excited about these activities and wants to devote as much of his time as possible to them. So, from a very early hour, the infant will be in top form ready to start the day: instead of spending long periods lying watching his hands he will want to be stimulated and want someone to come and see to him. Here are a few suggestions which may help the baby to sleep longer. He should be put to bed fairly late, played with a lot before his meal, given a soothing bath and put to bed with his face down. Sometimes nothing works and the parent has to be patient. Fortunately, not all babies are as demanding as this and some are quite happy to suck their fingers or chew a toy while waiting for their parents to get up.

Toys

— a crossbar (for the cot)
— brightly coloured cubes

— balls and reels for him to roll for the playpen
— little plastic toys (for the bath)
— little rubber toys (to suck)
— rags, rattles etc. (he can still use the toys from the previous month)
— a mirror (the baby looks at his reflection touches it).

6 MONTHS (24 WEEKS)

Postures

Trunk and head

Lying on his abdomen: the baby can raise himself on his hands (rather than on his forearms as during the previous month) and throw his head back (Fig. 2.22). His thorax and the upper part of his abdomen are raised above the plane of the bed.

Sitting: the infant can remain in a sitting position with a minimum of

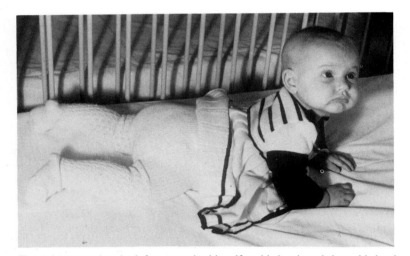

Fig. 2.22 6 months: the infant can raise himself on his hands and throw his head back.

support (perhaps some cushions to prop him up in his little chair) (Fig. 2.23).

Lying on his back: he can raise his head and shoulders above the plane of the bed in an effort to sit up without actually managing to do so. If his mother places her thumbs in his hands he grasps them and manages to sit up.

Limbs

He has stopped looking at his hands and he now catches hold of his feet (Fig. 2.24). Held upright he can bear a good part of his own weight and he skips about (this is the *'skipping'* stage) (Fig. 2.25).

The use of the hands

He can now grasp objects voluntarily with his whole hand. He can be observed to use an ulnar grip of the cube which he holds between the base of his thumb (on the ulnar side of the palm of the hand) and the three last fingers. He is able to hold two cubes and look at a third which has been put on a table. He will scrape the table with a knife and fork which he can hold in his hand.

Language

Between the 6th and 7th month is the age for *'babbling'* when the infant repeats in succession a simple consonant-vowel syllable: he can vary volume and speed of delivery and he has more control over what he says, when he is creating these melodies, which vary in length and intensity, the infant becomes aware of all the different tones he can produce and this is what inspires him to go back and start all over again. It is from these little exercises that he performs on his own that the baby derives the most enjoyment.

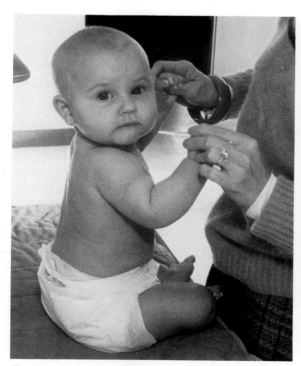

Fig. 2.23 6 months: the baby's back is much firmer and he can remain in the sitting position with a minimum of support.

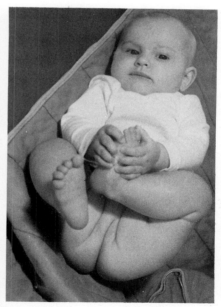

Fig. 2.24 6 months: the baby can catch hold of his feet.

Social development

The child is now perfectly capable of grasping objects voluntarily and he can pick up any (quite large) object he wants if it is placed near him. The infant is extremely active with objects as he was his 3rd month and he takes them to his mouth to find out exactly what they are. However 6-month-old babies have another reason for 'sucking' as this is the time when (in the case of some children) the first teeth are cut and their jaws are bothering them.

The baby also explores a new possibility: he can catch hold of his feet, touch them and look at them. He discovers them as he did his hands (see p. 24). He thus proceeds with the discovery of his body, piece by piece.

It is well known that the human voice is a very important factor in the child's environment. The infant is very aware of the volume and intonation of the voice. A sharp word, a harsh tone or a halting delivery can stop him in his tracks whereas he enjoys songs, music and rhymes as their rhythm encourages his language development. He may spend long periods of time listening to the radio or record player: in fact these might even be used to soothe him after a bout of tears. However if music is used either on unsuitable occasions or to excess it can have the opposite effect and excite the child.

The 6th month is also an important time for language development as this is when the baby starts to 'babble'. The child plays with syllables just as he plays with objects and he accompanies his vocal exercises with a wide variety of facial expressions and often also agitates his arms and legs which he uses as yet another means of communica-

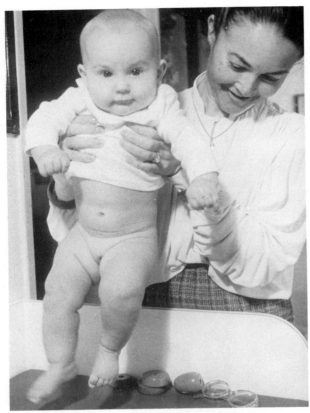

Fig. 2.25 6 months: held in a standing position the baby can bear a great part of his own weight.

This is a particularly crucial time for language development and the adult should not try to 'make' the child vocalise or make him vocalise for longer than he wants to as this might hinder the child's progress.

'The baby only starts to imitate others once he has imitated himself and therefore a parent should not interfere when a child is practising vocalisation; there are plenty of other occasions during the day when a mother can and should talk to the child.'[3]

Natalie (6 months old)

Natalie is in her cot; she has been doing her little vocal exercises for a solid hour. She does not tire of repeating the same chains of syllables and trills them to her heart's content. She thoroughly enjoys this; she hangs on to her very own words! But Sophy, her little sister, happens to come in and comes over to tickle her. Natalie screams with delight, plays with her for a while and when she goes, starts to yell. Mum comes in and to amuse her plays some soft music near her cot. Natalie calms down and anyway she has found a new game with her little feet which she grasps with her fists and tries to pull towards her.

tion! The baby is just as happy to go through this routine alone as in front of his family audience.

6 months marks the beginning of an important stage in his learning. He obviously still has a very limited vocabulary but this will increase monthly with his family's help. At this age it can be observed that girls (already) tend to babble more than boys and that a boy who babbles a lot is likely to be a fairly talkative child.

The baby generally enjoys meal times. If he sits near the family table he has the opportunity to seek attention, go through his little repertoire, banging his soup-covered spoon the the table or knocking over a glass while trying to get hold of it. Parents must be very patient with a baby of this age and be tolerant of his clumsiness as he is only trying to learn. The atmosphere at mealtimes should always be calm and relaxed as this is an ideal time for socialisation. The child really feels that he is part of the family. Nevertheless some mothers might prefer to have their evening meal later either for the reasons given on page 34 or because they want to have a little more peace when they are with the baby (the hubbub created by small brothers and sisters and their laughter and teasing might over-excite the baby who might then find it hard to get to sleep. Parents should seek a compromise between the needs of the baby, his temperament and family routine.

Toys

— crossbars
— teething rings
— chains of rings, keys, triangles or brightly coloured rubber discs
— attachable rattles (there are various models available)
— musical boxes.

7 MONTHS (28 WEEKS)

Postures

Trunk and head

Lying on his abdomen: he can roll over from his back on to his stomach (Fig. 2.26). He can raise a hand off the ground to grasp an object (Fig. 2.27).

Sitting: he can sit up without support for a brief period if he leans forward resting on the palms of his hands to stop himself from falling: this is known as the *parachutist* stage (Fig. 2.28). His torso is more supple and he can lean down to pick up an object with his hand.

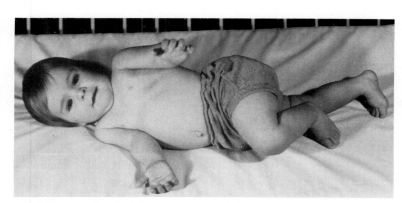

Fig. 2.26 7 months: the baby can roll from his back on to his stomach.

Fig. 2.27 7 months: the infant can raise a hand from the ground to grasp an object.

Limbs

When he is held upright he likes to be bounced: he will jump and crouch.

He is interested in his feet: he catches hold of them and can now 'suck his big toes'.

The use of the hands/understanding

The infant now grasps objects between the base of the thumb and the little finger (Fig. 2.29) and he makes a scratching movement to pick things up.

He can keep a cube in one hand without letting go if he is offered another.

He passes objects from one hand to the other and bangs them hard together or on the table.

He can let go of an object when he wants to: he can release objects at will but as yet it is a movement which lacks precision. He plays with his hands and feet and is aware of his own body. This is important for future motor development.

Language

A 7-month-old baby has made great progress in *babbling* (see p. 35). He often practises his new vocal skills; he uses them to attract his mother's attention. He has his own 'jargon' which he varies to express his own wishes.

If his mother does not come quickly enough he will babble louder and louder. If she spends too long talking to her neighbour he will try to drown out their voices. If he is on his own he will produce extended melodies.

He is particularly interested in music (as in the previous month)

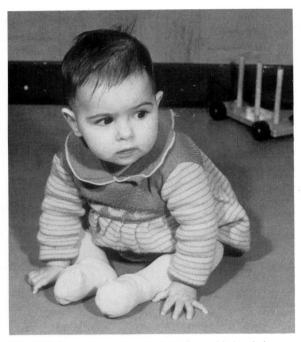

Fig. 2.28 7 months: sitting, the baby keeps his hands in front of him on the ground to prevent himself from falling (the parachutist position).

Fig. 2.29 7 months: the baby tries to grasp objects with the base of the thumb and the little finger.

and also in different kinds of noises from various sources.

Therefore parents should make every effort to provide him with enjoyment of this nature. They can buy him bells, a music box, even little birds and they might think of winding up an old clock as the baby will adore listening to it.

Christopher (7 months old)

Christopher is a happy active baby who over the last few weeks has got into the habit of being very demanding of his mother's attention. He weighs 7.2kg, has got a new front tooth and is having bother with his bottom gums. Christopher woke up several times last night having had a troubled night's sleep. Since 7 a.m. he has been playing quietly on his own chewing the edge of his bedcover and sucking his big toes.

Mum brought him his bottle at 8 a.m. which he drank at one go sitting up all by himself and then he played for ages with the teat. However things took a turn for the worse when Christopher threw his bottle out of the cot. It did not break but Mum got angry and gave him a scolding. Christopher cried for ages glancing up at his mother with sad reproachful eyes. He is now lying in his playpen but he has not got over it despite being surrounded by toys. He wants his mother to be there. Fortunately she is aware of this and comes over and plays a little game of rolling him over. Christopher laughs out loud and his mother hands him a little yellow duck. He grabs hold of it, clasps it to his chest, bangs it on the ground and passes it from one hand to the other. He shakes it, throws it away and then picks it up again. His Mum, happy to see him playing, goes away and keeps up a long conversation with him from the next room.

Social development

The 7th month is a transition period for the baby. He is able to play on his own but at the same time his mother's presence has become of crucial importance to him. He is as happy sitting as lying on his front and he is as content to play with his feet as with anything else.

He has a more intense relationship with his mother and he is better at discriminating between different faces: he is able to distinguish his mother from other people and he also begins to understand that he is *different* from his mother as she is *different* from him which brings him to the realisation that 'she is either there or she is not!' His affection for his mother increases his fears. He starts to be scared of new places and new people. He is no longer happy to gaze lovingly and admiringly at his mother, he leans his whole body towards her and wants to be in her arms. When he is picked up in her arms and is near her face he wants to explore every feature: nose, ears and mouth (which he likes putting his fingers into!). He also enjoys sucking his mother's face. She is very appreciative of these tokens of affection from her baby and this skin contact is very important for the development of both of them.

The baby can play on his own for long periods, sitting up with support in the corner of his playpen or in a little (preferably low) chair. Parents should make sure that the baby's back is always supported until he can sit up properly (or he will fatigue his back muscles). The baby can now spend long periods lying in his bed as he has discovered a new pastime: 'sucking his toes'. Thus continues his discovery of his body. The baby can also play while lying on his front (if something soft has been put under the playpen). These little exercises help to strengthen his muscles and to give him a feeling of freedom. He takes full advantage of this to bang about his toys, shake them, knock them together, pass them from hand to hand and swop them for others. He feels an urgent need to use his hands, 'it is the time when he uses his hands the most.'[1] He is better at manipulating objects. He picks up objects between his thumb and little finger. The infant makes a scratching or 'raking' movement to pick things up (with his arm flat against the table). He is becoming increasingly possessive about his toys (he has a way of clasping them to his chest which is particularly significant) and when he decides to 'throw' them down there is no doubt that it is a conscious decision on his part.

However, toys alone do not suffice and a 7-month-old baby will start crying as soon as his mother leaves the room. He would like her all to himself and have her with him at every moment of the day. Obviously a mother with a family cannot (and it is perhaps a good thing) be permanently at her baby's beck and call. It is best if she can talk to the baby while getting on with everything she has to do or even sing to him. Quite apart from the happy mood she will create, the baby will adore listening to her voice and a 'voice is another kind of presence'.

At 7 months when the baby cuts his first teeth he begins to enjoy the pleasure of *biting*. The baby can now be given a crust of bread or special biscuits which are made for babies of this age. Sugar lumps and sweets should be avoided at all cost as these might predispose the child towards having bad teeth. There are also some toys which can help at this time (see list on p. 40). It should also be remembered that all babies under the age of 12 months enjoy sucking their bottle. They can now hold it by themselves and they like to play with it after their feed and chew the teat. So even if the baby has progressed to using a spoon, parents should not be too strict and deprive their child of the pleasure he can derive from his bottle. All that is needed is to make the hole in the teat slightly larger for his feeds.

Toys

— teething rings
— chains of brightly coloured rubber rings, triangles, discs or keys
— music boxes
— plastic cubes
— rubber animals.

Fig. 2.30 8 months: the baby can remain *sitting* on his own!

8 MONTHS (32 WEEKS)

Postures

The muscles of the back and lumbar region have acquired good tone. The infant can *'sit up on his own'* (Fig. 2.30).
— On his back: he can sit up;
— On his abdomen: he can lift up his body by bearing his weight on his hands and the tips of his feet;
— He can easily *roll* over in both directions (back → front → back) (and this will provide a basis for his learning to *crawl* in a month's time).

The use of the hands/understanding

The infant becomes adept at grasping things with his thumb and little finger (see 7 months).

Between the 8th and 10th month the forefinger becomes more active and more supple.

If the child is holding two cubes and he is offered a third he can drop one in order to grasp the third (Fig. 2.31).

He plays at 'casting' things (he discovers a new property in objects, they make a 'noise' when they hit the ground!)

He can look for an object which is out of sight (like a rattle which has fallen down and which he wants back) (Fig. 2.32). If somebody takes an object which he is playing with and hides it behind a screen he will ask for it and stretch out a hand in the right direction.

Language

The child vocalises at the sight of people and objects and gives the impression that he is talking to them and wants to communicate with them.

He tries to modulate his sound combinations and will eventually produce the monosyllables 'da', 'ma', 'ga' and then 'pa'. The sounds he makes are virtually impossible to decipher but they are the beginnings of language. The infant talks to

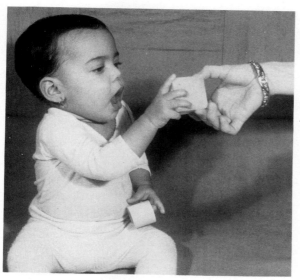

Fig. 2.31 8 months: the baby can let go of a cube he is holding in his hand to grasp hold of another.

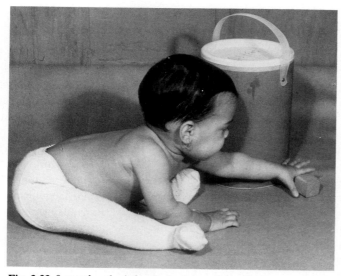

Fig. 2.32 8 months: the infant looks for an object hidden out of sight.

himself and talks to others and sometimes backs this up with gestures and expressions to make what he is saying more explicit!

This is also an important stage in language development. Parents should talk to their child as often as possible and should help him to extend his range. They should take care not to deform the words they use (by talking 'baby language') and instead build on the same sounds as the baby is already making. There is an art to knowing how to create the right atmosphere: getting the child into the right mood for expressing himself and not over-whelming him with bookish language. Instead the parents should linguisti-cally exploit his daily rituals when they are bathing him, changing his nappy, putting him to bed. The infant should be encouraged to enjoy language as he should associate it with the feelings of wellbeing and of communicating intimately with someone dear to him.

Helen (8 months old)

Helen is sitting in the corner of her playpen sulking after a long bout of tears which was brought on by her mother going out. Nicky is looking after the baby for the first time and does not know quite what toy to give the baby. First she finds some cubes and puts them in the playpen but Helen makes no effort to pick them up. She then offers the baby a musical box but to no avail. She finally manages to win the baby's attention by offering her her teddy. At this, Helen, still looking a bit glum, starts a long monologue which Nicky unfortunately has to interrupt because it is time for the baby's feed. Helen screams and Nicky can only finally persuade her to eat after having first fed her teddy.

When Mum gets home that evening she hears that her daughter has not been very co-operative . . . the only person worthy of her attention has been her 'little friend'.

Social development

Now that the baby can sit up on his own he is one step nearer independence. He is able to take full advantage of his playpen and he will try out all kinds of positions. He can now control the muscles of his abdomen and back and this enables him to *roll* over which he finds fun. He can easily lean over to pick up his toys and then sit back up again.

Some very active children already manage a crawling position but the majority do not reach this stage until the 9th (or 10th) month. When the baby is undressed he will often perform some quite remarkable feats like supporting his entire weight on his hands and the tips of his toes alone. He dislikes being undressed and will wriggle like an eel. The infant is never still for a moment. He is eager to demonstrate his new-found skills and plays from morning till night. He is more skilful with his hands and likes to have something in each hand which he takes turns in taking to his mouth.

He also likes *casting* objects to hear the noise they make when they fall. This tells him how hard he can throw. This activity is particularly demanding on those who are in the vicinity as they are required to retrieve the objects.

The *mirror* game is another favourite game of 8-month-old babies (Fig. 2.33). The infant is fascinated by his own reflection: he smiles at it, watches it, talks to it and even kisses it. If he sees his foot in the mirror he will immediately touch his own to compare them. This game enables him to gain a better perception of himself. He can see himself move.

However 8 months is a difficult age as the infant is going through what the psychologists call a 'crisis of anxiety'. He is psychologically totally dependant on his mother and as he can easily distinguish her from

Fig. 2.33 8 months: the infant is fascinated in playing with a *mirror*.

other people this means that she cannot be replaced by someone else. The infant's happiness depends on whether the 'object'★ of his love is present or not. He is desperate for the reassurance of his mother's presence. He is very demanding of her and this changes his behaviour with other people: he cries when strangers are present (especially if they try to pick him up!); he is scared of being left without his mother and if she has to leave him he cries bitterly.

Parents must make every effort to be understanding during this difficult period and try to help the child through it without too many upsets. They should avoid picking him up

★Object: word used by psychologists meaning goal towards which a child's love is directed.

and mothering him too often as this will lead him into bad habits but they should spare their child those crying fits which Montessori has called 'the first sickness of the soul'.[4] Parents should avoid leaving their child on his own with people he scarcely knows or in a new environment. The baby does not understand why he has been *separated*. The fact that an 8-month-old baby can start crying when he sees his mother dressed up ready to go out is proof in itself that he is capable of anticipating what is going to happen: what he does not know is whether she will return and so he feels that she is *abandoning* him.

Parents are also strongly advised not to send an 8-month-old baby to a creche (except in unavoidable circumstances) as this is psychologically a critical period: the child's development is extremely vulnerable at this time.

Parents should also avoid taking their baby to social gatherings. The strange faces, loud voices, laughter and movement will disturb the baby and he is liable to become over-excited: indeed 'the instability of the infant's emotional make-up is demonstrated in the 8th month by the close interdependence of laughter and tears'.[1]

Games

The is the ideal time to buy the child a teddy who will be a faithful friend and keep him company when his mother is not there. He will be there at times of distress and the baby will want to take him everywhere, sleep with him, cuddle him and chew him. Teddy will assume the role of 'substitute mother' and help the child become more detached from his mother (see the bear as a symbolic game, p. 96).

An 8-month-old baby may easily become attached to some other object: a rag, a blanket, an old nappy which he will want to take everywhere with him and any adult who dares remove it from him will unleash a fit of bitter tears. These objects are really forms of compensation; they enable the child to carry around with him a bit of his surroundings, a bit of his mother. In fact, he finds in them a symbol of emotional security in this new frightening world he is starting to explore.

Parents should not belittle these fetishes: they are valuable in that they help the child to cope with frustration and inevitable separations from his mother. The baby has had to make a real effort to transfer his

affections elsewhere and he needs support.

Spitz has observed that 'the anxiety experienced in the 8th month is the foundation for the child's emotional development'; the child tries in every conceivable way to replace his mother in her absence.

Other toys at 8 months

— teething rings
— chains of brightly coloured rings, triangles, discs or keys
— music boxes
— plastic cubes
— rubber animals.

9 MONTHS (36 WEEKS)

Postures

Head and trunk

Lying on abdomen: he tries to *crawl* but goes backwards (he starts by using his arms and will soon take his weight on his knees) (Fig. 2.34).
— He likes to roll over in order to move about.
— He can lean forward and then sit back up again but he cannot yet lean over sideways.

Fig. 2.34 9 months: the infant tries to 'crawl' (but often goes backwards).

Limbs

He can stand up by holding on to his playpen or a piece of furniture (Fig. 2.35). He sticks out his buttocks to keep his balance, remains standing for a few moments but then falls.

The use of the hands/understanding

— He can pick up objects the size of a button between the base of his thumb and his forefinger (this enables him to do much more with his hands) (Fig. 2.36).

— He can compare two cubes by bringing them together.
— He is learning to hand a toy to his parents: at first he refuses to let go of the toy but later he will let go and hand it over.
— He can ring a bell.
— He can catch hold of a ring by its string.

Language

At this age the infant will either continue to practise 'talking' as has already been mentioned (p. 40) or he will move on to actual speech and start to say his first words. What are these long-awaited first words?

In most cases they are repeated syllables drawn from a very basic phonetic vocabulary: the most common first word is 'mama' followed by 'papa' etc. There is no telling whether the child's first word will be 'mama' or 'papa' or 'dada' or 'mumum' (or anything) but it is a fact that 'mama' is generally the first word said: this is perhaps because it is such an emotionally charged word or perhaps simply because it is easier to pronounce than 'dada'. These are probably the reasons why it is the

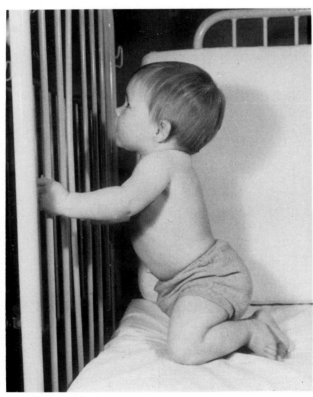

Fig. 2.35 9 months: the infant can stand up by holding on to the furniture (but he has a poor sense of balance).

first word in the vocabulary of most children (of a number of nationalities!).

This stage of language ability can be reached at any time between the 9th and 15th month (approximately). Thus it is very difficult to pinpoint the precise stage of the baby's development.

Jack (9 months old)

Jack has got stuck between two pieces of furniture and he is yelling desperately for his mother to come and help. His enormous progress in getting about leads him on to new exploits which do not always have a happy ending! Jack needs space and refuses

to go into his playpen. His Mum is very obliging and leaves him in the front room. This gives him much more scope to move around. Nevertheless Jack can sit quietly for long periods if he is given objects to play with. It does not matter how small they are, he will lay claim to them and enjoys making up games with a dice, a cotton reel, a shoe box. His mother keeps a watchful eye on him. Jack must need to see her pop in from time to time as any time she seems to be too far away he shouts for her to come back and 'she' comes. And usually, to their mutual enjoyment, she plays a little game of 'peekaboo' which the baby loves to play over and over again.

Social development

The 9th month is a time when the

baby becomes extremely active again. He becomes more skilled in using his hands and he can now pick up objects with the tip of his thumb and the tip of his forefinger (like a marble, a button or a piece of string). Although he is still clumsy in picking up objects, the use of his hands improves and he will derive enormous pleasure from this. He will be very aware of the movement of his thumb and forefinger and he will practise turning objects over in all directions. He will willingly drop objects just for the sheer pleasure of picking them up again. The fact that he can now separate his thumb and forefinger is a milestone in the development of the child's use of his hands. An active child will also explore to the full the entire range of movements he can now make: he can crawl by using his hands and by flexing his legs. He very often starts by crawling backwards (his muscles are stronger for pushing him backwards than for going forwards).

In order to encourage the child's progress a small toy can be placed just out of reach and the added incentive of curiosity will ensure that the baby soon reaches it. Since it is difficult to keep a watch on what a child of this age is doing some mothers still resort to a playpen: it may be too small but it does give a sense of security. There are a (very) few models of playpens which are expandable and these provide much greater space than is customary but if this has not been acquired at the outset the additional expense is not justified by the length of time the baby will use it for. It is reassuring to know that even if the baby is given free rein he will not stray very far as he is still extremely *dependent* on his mother. As we have already seen in the case of an 8-month-old baby

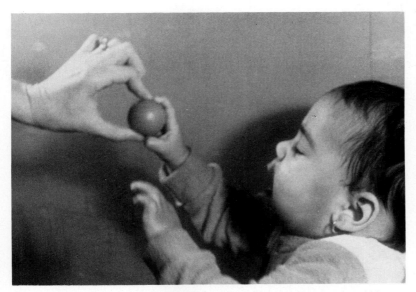

Fig. 2.36 9 months: he can grasp an object between the base of his thumb and his forefinger.

(see p. 41) this stage is quite a lengthy one (often lasting until the baby is 1 year old). The baby will curb his activity as his mother's image is constantly in his mind and he will keep returning towards her as if he does not want to lose her from his sight.

The fact that he wants to remain in the proximity of his mother does not mean that his progress is in any way affected and many babies of 9 months can be seen trying to stand up on their own with the help of the playpen or some piece of furniture. The infant's balance is still insecure and he readily falls backwards on to his bottom (he falls forward much less frequently as he sticks out his buttocks in an effort to keep his balance). These exploits will lead him on to new challenges and also present him with new fears. He is therefore desperately reliant on his mother to extricate him from awkward positions. Babies rarely come to any harm when exploring all their new potential but if a mother wants to teach the baby how to sit back down again she could teach him the following game: hold the baby upright on a double bed and try to make him bend at the waist while holding his hands in front of him. Then jerk his hands downwards and he will find himself sitting down. Obviously this game has a number of variations which can be introduced and even if the baby does not learn anything immediately (because his natural development cannot be hurried) he will at least have thoroughly enjoyed it. Another game which babies are extremely fond of is 'peekaboo'. The baby adores hiding his face behind a cover or a scarf and then throwing it off with squeals of delight every time his mother asks 'where is baby?'. He likes his mother to play

as well and every time her face reappears he is delighted. In playing this apparently simple game the baby finds the security and reassurance he needs. He is able to orchestrate a separation in the knowledge (he can now anticipate events) that it will not last! He is acquiring his own independence.

Games

The best games at 9 months, other than those mentioned above, are those which enable the child to try out his new motor abilities.

He can be given:
— cubes to be placed in a bowl
— coloured balls
— coloured sewing reels.

10 MONTHS (40 WEEKS)

Postures

The baby can now *walk on all fours* (unlike his first attempts at crawling the baby always moves forward) (Fig. 2.37). The infant can *stand up* on his own by holding on to furniture (Fig. 2.38) and he can raise one foot and walk a few steps while still holding on to furniture but he frequently falls.

The use of the hands/understanding

He can pick up objects more accurately between the tip of his thumb

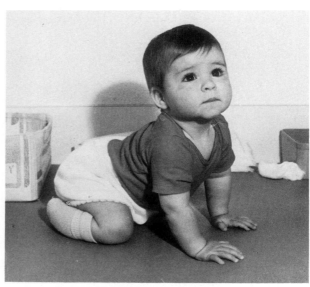

Fig. 2.37 10 months: the infant can now crawl

Fig. 2.38 10 months: the infant can walk a few steps while holding on to the furniture.

and the tip of his forefinger.

He can pick up small objects and hand them to someone. He will continue to take objects to his mouth until he is 1 year old.

He can 'wave goodbye' and clap his hands.

He can distinguish between a container and its contents: he enjoys *putting objects into* boxes and then *taking* them out again.

Between the ages of 10 and 11 months he acquires a sense of three dimensionality (see p. 49).

When playing with a 'posting box' he can remove a round shape from its hole.

He can drink from a cup or beaker by himself.

He pulls at people's clothes to attract their attention.

Language

If the child has reached the stage immediately prior to actual speech he will be using monosyllables or segmented syllables (see p. 40).

He can understand the gist of a phrase and often makes a gesture to illustrate a word (for example, if his mother tells him to say 'bye-bye' to someone he will wave his hand).

He is sensitive to the tone of the voice and will cry if spoken sharply to or scolded by someone close to him.

At this age, one word can have a whole variety of meanings: the word is a *symbol*. The baby may say 'milk' not only to refer to milk but, by extension, to any other kind of liquid. He may use 'dada' for all men etc.

Here again, the parents should, without forcing their child, help him to learn to use the appropriate vocabulary. Words should always be illustrated by gestures so that the child can link words with their contexts. It is obvious that if the first animal that the child learns the word for is a dog then all other animals are going to be dogs too until he has learnt that they too have names and this not only takes time but also real situations.

Emma (10 months old)

Mum is annoyed and Emma cannot stay still for a minute. She crawls around all over the place on all fours. She wants to be able to see everything and to discover everything. From time to time she tries to stand up but repeatedly falls. What's the use? It is much faster on all fours anyway. What's that cable and that socket with the three holes? I'll just stick my finger in to explore. Oh, here's Mum, back again to tell me not to. It's impossible to find out anything when everybody's always telling you not to touch! I'm going to cry. Then maybe Mum will play my favourite game to cheer me up. The game with the big coloured plastic rings which I can put in the little shoe box we found yesterday in the bedroom cupboard. Or she might even give me the big china bowl to put all my little red and blue cubes into. Mum doesn't give me anything of the sort as it is mealtime and I'm put in my little chair and have to wait for my parents. It's a good thing that there is something new on the table for me to play with while I'm waiting.

Social development

A 10-month-old child is extending his motor abilities: he can *walk on all fours*. Crawling is no longer good enough for him. He wants to move on a stage and discover a new way of getting about. Walking on all fours is not easy as the infant has alternately to move his arms and legs in rhythm and this makes it a decisive step towards walking.

The infant will initially support himself on his hands and knees (he will not be able to support himself on his hands and the soles of his feet until the following month). He will practise for hours on end. He will be unsteady at first, but he will soon become stronger and manage to make his way around the flat.

This is his favourite exercise as his timid efforts at standing up and his subsequent falls frighten him: this makes him all the more eager to come to grips with his 'ground-work'. There are some babies who enjoy moving around on their buttocks or pulling themselves along by one arm and swimming with their bodies. The baby needs scope for his motor development as he is becoming more agile, more curious and he wants to explore everything. So care should be taken with anything at ground level which could prove dangerous: electric sockets, the cable on the iron, products kept under the sink.

He is so enthusiastic about his achievements at ground level that he can even manage to carry an object while walking on all fours. If he is agile he might manage to reach up to a magazine rack (he will enjoy tearing its contents apart) or the drawer of a sideboard (which he will start to empty).

He should not be held back too much: these activities mean a lot to him and therefore anything fragile should be kept out of the reach of his irrepressible enthusiasm.

The infant also enjoys exploring things with his fingers especially objects he has managed to take from his mother: he holds them firmly between thumb and forefinger, he curves his hands around objects (small and large), he gazes at them for long periods and feels them all over fingering holes and crevices (often infants are aware of the third dimension by the 10th month) and then throws them to the ground to check how solid they are. This shows how eager he is to discover the world around him and so the throwing of objects should not be looked on as being aggressive or destructive.

The baby should be in a stimulating environment and should not be asked to 'stop that' too often as this will curb his development and give rise to fear and timidity.

This is why children in large families make greater progress than others of the same age as their mothers have plenty to do and thus allow them to do more and they also have older children to involve them in their games. This does not mean to say that such a young child should be left unsupervised or that his calls should go unheeded in the hope of making him fight for his independence . . . quite the opposite; the child needs supervised freedom and an appropriate response to each of his demands if his personality is to develop in the best way possible. The mother should make sure that all her child's negative emotions are transformed into positive experiences. If, for example, the baby falls awkwardly when he is involved in doing something he should be picked up, cuddled, laughed with and then faced with the same situation again so that he can learn to cope with it. This is a way of helping him come to terms with the risks involved and is better than dramatising a fall.

The mother should learn to guide her child's progress and she should find ways of stimulating rather than inhibiting the child. It is as easy for a child to sense one's fears as one's hopes and this obviously influences the child.

Games

— coloured plastic rings

— plain cubes or cubes for slotting into a 'posting box'
— beakers which fit into each other
— boxes, cartons, pictures (educational games)
— and some of the toys from the previous month.

11 MONTHS (44 WEEKS)

Postures

He starts to take his first steps. He can now walk if an adult holds him by both hands (Fig. 2.39).

He can walk on his own by holding on to the furniture. He is more confident on all fours. He walks 'like a bear' up on his hands and feet.

The use of the hands/understanding

The infant becomes better at holding objects between the thumb and forefinger (p. 46) and finds it easier to put his fingers into this position.

At the age of 10–11 months 'the child enjoys pointing an inquisitive finger at objects (Fig. 2.40) and will readily explore its *third dimension*: holes, grooves, cavities. As he has better control over his hands he can

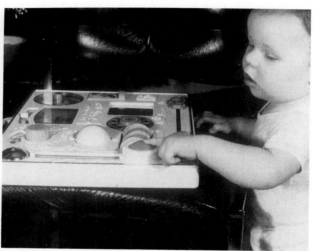

Fig. 2.40 10/11 months: the infant likes 'pointing' an inquisitive forefinger.

Fig. 2.39 11 months: the infant can now walk if an adult holds him by both hands.

appreciate depth, solidity, the container and the content, the top and the bottom, the side, the inside and the outside, the different elements and the whole'[1].

'The child is aware of 'two' and 'one'. He can bring together two objects to make one (Fig. 2.41). His awareness of duality is still rather vague but he feels a great need to bring things together.'[1]

He can throw a ball back to an adult who is playing with him and if he is sitting down he will turn his body right round to catch a ball which is thrown to him (Fig. 2.42).

Language

Between the 11th and 15th month the infant will start to use fairly meaningful one and two word sentences. These are short sentences of the nature of 'milk all gone'. This jargon is not yet based on the actual meaning of the words but rather on context.

To help her child's progress the mother should always link words to a specific context. For example, if a child says 'dada byebye' it is because he has heard his mother say this to his father every morning.

It is through *words and gestures* and *words in context* that the child will learn to relate words and to develop intellectually.

Furthermore, even if the child has not yet started or is still very poor at producing language, the more he hears his parents repeat certain phrases the more he will select and store a linguistic repertoire which one day he will use successfully.

Gregory (11 months old)

Gregory sets off to explore the family flat at a very early hour. He gets himself up into a 'bearwalk' which his small brothers find

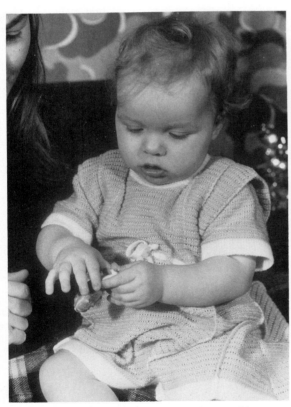

Fig. 2.41 11 months: the infant likes to bring two objects together to make one.

Fig. 2.42 11 months: the infant likes playing ball with an adult.

hilarious. They often tease him and set up roadblocks for him. Gregory, undeterred, shakes his head and presses on. There is altogether too much on his plate without distractions. There are so many objects within arm's reach in all the rooms he can get at; also drawers and boxes filled with all manner of wonderful things.

There is so much to see, to grasp hold of and to explore with one's fingers, so many things to hold on to. 'I'm sure that table wasn't there yesterday?' It is as if Gregory were thinking: 'This world is definitely much too big for me, I'm scared I might get lost. Oh, there's Mum! I'll just push this ball under the sofa so she can go and get it. I might even get her to play 'hide and seek'. That would be nice!'

Social development

The 11th month can seem like a transition period. The infant will start to capitalise on his motor abilities to widen his intellectual horizons.

He now has a much better visual memory and he can now observe details which formerly escaped him and which sometimes escape even adults.

In his mind he perceives things as 'wholes': this is why he is disturbed when certain elements are 'missing'. Montessori believes that the child has a very deep-seated sense of *order*. 'A small girl some months old had a crying fit when a friend of her mother put an umbrella on her bedroom table. Every attempt was made to find out why she was crying so that she could be comforted but to no avail. Suddenly her mother thought of taking the umbrella into the next room and the little girl stopped crying instantly.' The umbrella was an alien object which did not fit into the infant's scheme of things. The infant feels a need to order things in his mind.

The infant also memorises the qualities of certain objects. If, for example, a relatively heavy object is about to be thrown on the ground the infant will screw up his eyes. He can *anticipate* the noise the object will make by knowing how heavy it is. Likewise, while a child is learning to stand he will differentiate between those pieces of furniture capable of supporting his weight and those which are less reliable. Thus he will select what furniture is going to see him through his first steps! The infant also learns to discriminate better between container and content (he can put tiny objects into a box, take them out again and then repeat this). He can take objects in either hand, weigh them up and compare them. At this age he loves differentiating between 'two' and 'one' and between the 'part' and the 'whole'. He is already developing fairly complex mental procedures to enable him to deal with the objects he uses.

He has mastered the art of crawling and is '*walking like a bear*' with his bottom stuck out behind him. He can stand up from this position and this is preliminary to actually walking. Some active children try to walk sideways while holding on to a sofa while others start to walk with an adult holding their hands. The infant is especially fond of those games where he has to stand up and play 'peekaboo'. This is an excellent exercise for improving muscle control and making him more supple.

If the infant decides he does not want to do any activity that you have decided on he is perfectly capable of saying no and shaking his head. He might, however, just be saying no for the sheer pleasure of practising a new word and not by way of refusal. It is much easier to say no by word and gesture than to say yes.

Nevertheless, he is perfectly aware of what he is not allowed to do. *Imitation* is an important element in the life of an infant of this age. This is how he learns many new things. He watches people eat, put their cups to their lips, hold a fork, wipe their hands and he wants to do likewise. He may also pick up people's attitudes and traits of personality. This may indeed be amusing but he should not be encouraged in this. It is better for him to develop his own personality. The infant studies movements and he likes playing with a ball, rolling it and hiding it under the sofa and then going to find it. Like the game of 'peekaboo' (p. 46) the game of 'hide and seek' fascinates the infant and if he is asked to fetch an object (which of course he has seen being hidden) he will go and fetch it and this will stimulate not only his motor development but also his memory of the object. This game is also reassuring for the infant who can think 'You cannot see it from here but I know where it is!' This helps him feel that he is in control of his environment, that he is on steady ground. In this connection Montessori[4] talks of an experiment Piaget carried out on his child: 'The teacher hid an object under the cushion of one armchair and then moved it to another armchair to make the child use logic to find it but each time the infant picked up the cushion of the first armchair and said 'Not there'. In exasperation, the teacher lifted up the cushion of the second chair and showed the child the object. Without a flicker of surprise the child picked up the object and put it back under the first cushion to show his father where it should be hidden.' The child was not as interested in looking for the object as in finding it in its right place.

Games (other than those described above)

— a variety of cubes
— beakers which fit into each other
— pyramids of rings
— balls of various sizes.

12 MONTHS (48 WEEKS)

Postures

The infant *walks* with an adult *holding* one hand (Fig. 2.43).

He might start to 'walk by himself' between the ages of 12 and 15 months (initially he walks un-

Fig. 2.43 12 months: the infant walks with an adult holding one hand.

steadily and frequently falls).

He pushes chairs to help himself learn to walk.

He can move forward on his buttocks with the help of his hands.

He can lean down from an upright position to pick up a toy.

He can throw his head right back when drinking and finish off the last drop.

The use of the hands/understanding

He practises *releasing an object with precision* (Fig. 2.44) between the ages of 12 and 15 months (his ability to do this depends on how well he can control the extensor muscles of his upper limbs).

He likes throwing objects one by one.

He practises '*kicking*' a ball back (his ability to do this depends on how well he can control the extensor muscles of his lower limbs).

He likes *fitting* objects into each other.

He likes putting baskets, hats and bags on his head.

He likes putting things into containers and taking them out (games with containers and contents) (Fig. 2.45).

If he is shown what to do he will make his first scribbles (see p. 86).

The 'posting box': he will put a round shape into the appropriate hole on a board.

Language

Between the ages of 12 and 15 months is the age for *general meaningful language*' which will be gradually mastered by the child.

He can say two or three phrases of the nature of 'dada bye-bye', 'milk allgone' which are closely

Fig. 2.44 Between 12 and 15 months the child practises releasing an object with precision.

Fig. 2.45 12 months: the child enjoys putting objects into a container and taking them out again.

linked to a context either in the past or the present.

Not all 1-year-old infants reach this stage of language development which, as we have already mentioned, can be reached at any time between 11 and 15 months. Nevertheless any 1-year-old child ought to understand a number of phrases used by his parents and at least reply by deed if not by word. If, for example, the parents say 'Come and give me a kiss' or 'Go and look for your teddy' the child should act or at least show that he has understood.

Alan (12 months old)

Alan weighs 10½ kg and has seven milk teeth. For the last quarter of an hour he has been playing with his posting games but he is losing patience. He prefers playing 'upsie-daisy' which at least teaches him how to walk. He is on the verge of those first steps his Mum and Dad are so eager for. He seems to be saying 'Well, perhaps tomorrow?'. It must be so simple to walk without anybody holding your hands. 'What a pity that there is no garden! There is not enough space in here!' 'Oh, there is the television! What luck! Robert and Jackie are clapping and I'm going to join in the racket and have a romp with them. I'm going to have some fun now!' But his brother and sister show not the least interest in him and by way of consolation he goes to the kitchen and takes some biscuits from the kitchen table and throws them, one, two, three on to the floor. Mum has just made his tea and he cannot miss that! He has not been spotted, so he makes off quickly and the only one to witness the episode is the cat. But where are they all? They cannot possibly not hear my 'Mama', 'Dada'. Walking is great fun but not when you are all on your own.

Social development

The first birthday is a family occasion. The parents are very excited about it. They can count their infant's age now in years rather than months! The first birthday does not, however, appear to mark any mile-stone in psycho-motor development. Often it is some months before any major change becomes apparent. Between the ages of 12 and 15 months the infant is indeed 'on his way to acquiring new abilities'[1]. It is a period when the infant develops his linguistic and motor skills. No child has the same rate of progress. Some have already mastered 'general meaningful language' whereas others will need to wait until they are 15 months old. Likewise some children learn to walk at 12 months while others are still 'walking like a bear'.

Nevertheless, the progress that is made at 12 months should not be underestimated: an infant of this age will improve his use of thumb and forefinger and practise releasing objects with precision. (This ability depends on how well the infant can control the extensor muscles of his upper limbs.) The baby can use a fork, put his spoon into his feed, drink properly out of a cup and pick up crumbs one by one. In fact, he likes all small objects which he can pick up one by one, put into a container, take out again one by one and start all over again.

This action is, in fact, a very rudimentary form of counting.[1] The fact that the baby has better control over the extensor muscles of his upper limbs enables him to kick a ball with increased force. At the age of 12 months he is only really starting to learn how to kick. What he is able to do is to jig about in time with the beat of pop music and he finds this all the easier if he has brothers and sisters to copy or even a dancer on the television screen. He has a truly remarkable 'gift of imitation'. If he is applauded or an interest is taken in him he will repeat his exploits as he is becoming increasingly aware of adult approval.

He likes 'playing to an audience'. This does not mean that he is in any way vain or an exhibitionist as all infants are attention-seeking at this age as it helps them to develop their own personalities. They are also increasingly aware of the 'self' as compared with other people. Imitation leads to the discovery of the other. At the age of 12 months there is a better relationship between the infant and the adult. A 1-year-old infant is gradually learning to detach himself from his mother. The crisis of anxiety (p. 42) (which can last between the ages of 8 and 12 months) tends to diminish and this means that the infant can become more sociable and good-natured. The infant needs other people to help him to walk, to play with him on their laps, to pick up the objects he throws down, to play hide-and-seek with him and to provide an audience. This new interest in other people does not mean that he is any less self-centred. He only learns to hand over an object on request because he knows that it will be handed back to him. He gives in order to receive. He has a vested interest in being sociable as it allows him to display his talents. A 'baby-walker'* is ideal at this age: it delights the baby and reassures his parents. It provides greater support than any hand and gives the baby the confidence he needs to learn to walk. Often when a baby learns to walk, with all the feverish activity that this entails, he will sleep for shorter periods of experience some difficulty in getting to sleep in the evening. A similar problem may

*Baby-walker: a canvas seat fixed to a support on wheels which enables the baby to move about upright and allows him to sit down when he wishes.

arise with his eating habits. The infant will spend longer actually using his hands and therefore eat less. He would much rather play at picking up crumbs and putting them in his mouth one by one or by tracing patterns with his fingers in his baby food (a foretaste of creativity to come). It should be understood why he does this and he should be prevented from making a mess without stifling his new talents. Many mothers are so concerned about the amount of food the baby should be eating that they are completely unaware of the value to the baby of actually exploring what he is about to eat. If the baby refuses point blank to eat, he should not be forced as he is likely to make an issue out of his refusal by closing his mouth, spitting the food out again, throwing his head right back or acting the clown. He is displaying his independence. At 12 months the baby is extremely imaginative in the way he finds to say no. Care should be taken that mealtimes do not become an occasion for family rows.

Games

— a bottle and small balls which can be put inside
— small balls which can be threaded on to a string, counting frames, larger balls
— pyramids of brightly coloured rings and cubes
— beakers and boxes which fit inside each other
— books with thick pages.

15 MONTHS

Postures

The infant can *walk by himself* (Fig. 2.46).
— He can climb the stairs on all fours.
— He can kneel unaided.
— He can stand up on his own but his sense of balance is still poor and he falls.

The use of the hands/understanding

The infant likes *throwing objects down, throwing them back* to people and *pushing* (Fig. 2.47).
— He can release objects from his hands with even greater precision.
— He is better at throwing a ball back to someone (but he often falls over).
— He can put a button into a bottle (Fig. 2.48).

Fig. 2.46 15 months: the infant can *walk by himself*.

Fig. 2.47 15 months: the infant likes *pushing* objects.

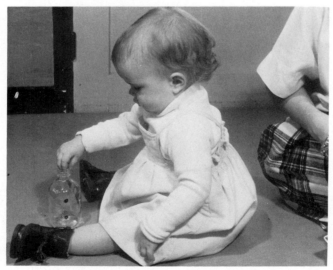

Fig. 2.48 15 months: the infant can put a button into a bottle.

— He can hold his spoon (but he puts it into his mouth upside down).
— He can ask for objects by pointing to them.
— He can turn the pages of a picture book (but skips several pages when leafing through a book).
— He can reproduce a line made by an adult on a piece of paper.
— *Building games*: he can build a tower two cubes high.
— *Posting games*: he can 'post' the appropriate block into a hole of its own size and shape.

Language

Between the ages of 15 and 24 months the infant improves his use of 'general meaningful language' for example: 'Sophy doll broken' which means 'Sophy's doll is broken.' Also, the infant generally orders his words according to how important they are to him: he often puts himself first followed by the object which is closest to him and often a word which 'clarifies' the situation to the adult will come last.

He can modulate his voice better and this helps him to express his feelings more easily.

All this age parents should not be too eager for him to speak properly.

He will not be able to use the verb or to produce a sentence which sounds completely like speech until he is aged 2½ to 3 years old.

He will draw on all his linguistic capital to give a running commentary to certain actions.

The parents should speak to their child often using sentences which are short, simple and also correct: 'Look at Mum', 'She's getting washed' 'Baby also has to get washed.' Although this language

may appear simplistic, it is through hearing words repeated in context that the baby will overcome this long-awaited linguistic hurdle. If, on the other hand, the parents impose language on the child and there is too great a gap between the model they set and what the child is capable of achieving, the child might become inhibited and actually regress.

Natalie (15 months old)

Natalie is a lively little girl. She walks well, weighs 11½ kg, has 8 teeth and can make herself understood by short little sentences which she often accompanies by gestures. She potters around the house, often bumping into furniture and falling over. Instead of starting to cry she tries to stand up again but this is not always easy. She often enjoys pushing a piece of furniture from one room to another which is not always to her mother's delight! But what she likes best is Dad's wastepaper bin which she regularly empties in order to put it on her head. Her father comes in and scolds her. Natalie cries and then calms down. It's not the only pastime in the world and the moment her father's back is turned she tries to console herself by picking up his alarm clock. It is such fun to throw and she loves twiddling with the buttons and what if the alarm goes off? But Adrian, her big brother, takes it from her before she even has a chance to throw it.

Natalie screams with rage and her mother immediately tries to comfort her with a biscuit and takes her for her bath. That is also another favourite pastime. Natalie likes the water and sometimes splashes around in it too much for her own good, puts the soap on her head, hurls it on to the floor and sucks the shower attachment. When her mother wants to lift her out of the bath she whines and wriggles. Her mother has to get a good grip of her if she is to be dressed at all! Mum finds her very hard to control and has to use all her imagination to keep her daughter occupied.

Social development

The infant can walk at last. He can control his body upright and uses this new ability as a basis for launching an attack on his surround-

ings (seen, as it were, from a new vantage point!). The infant is aware of his new capabilities and these have a direct influence on his personality. He is increasingly less willing to accept family restrictions. He might (in his own interest) be forbidden to do certain things at the very moment when he is determined to do them all by himself. This is often a difficult time for both the baby and his family.

Staying upright becomes an exhilarating game. He sets off, stops, sets off again and then falls over. He should never be laid down to be dressed: if he is he will start to yell. It is better for him to play an active role: he can lift his foot, stretch out an arm. All this motor activity will lead him on to new discoveries like, for example, climbing the stairs on all fours (he will not be able to negotiate the stairs upright until the next stage in his development). If the stair is only a few steps high he can be left to practise on his own. If not, a close watch should be kept over him. He cannot yet make his way downstairs and he is frightened of the drop. To avoid accidents it is best to put a gate at the bottom (although this deprives the baby of such fun!). If the mother has time, she can teach her child to climb up and down the stairs. His excitement is a prelude to great things to come.

If he is left on his own the infant will practise various exercises from the standing position. He will stretch upwards, kneel down, manage to pick up his toys from under his chair and try to stand up again on his own. This may prove more difficult and he often falls over on to the ground.

He will quickly overcome these minor difficulties over the weeks to come. In the meantime, practice is the most important thing and his 'baby-walker' will soon have outlived its usefulness. The infant refuses to be hampered by it. If he needs support he is perfectly capable of finding it for himself by pushing about a piece of furniture. Parents should not be angry when they see their best piece of Chippendale being bumped around the house. The infant does not always make the most appropriate choice. In this case he should be given a less fragile (but fairly heavy) chair so that he can practise pushing. This is how he builds up necessary strength in his muscles.

Parents should not worry if the child walks with his legs apart as this helps him to keep his balance at the beginning. He should be bought good shoes which support the soles of his feet. These will both help him walk and guard against flatfootedness. Over recent months the infant has been becoming increasingly sociable. He needs other people to play with, to climb on to their laps, to play 'peekaboo', to take him out in his pushchair, to take the sticks he hands them (without, as when he was 12 months old, expecting them to be handed back) and to dance with.

He starts to call for the type of activity that the creche can provide: he starts to play with building blocks, posting boxes, and he likes scribbling and picture books (he likes turning the pages and is interested in the pictures: dogs, cats, etc.)

The adult should not try to force the child's development. At 15 months he is only just out of babyhood. Obviously he wants his independence but he is not capable of doing everything for himself. At mealtimes, he still holds his spoon upside down and puts as much food on to the table as he does into his mouth (Fig. 2.49). He might show his mother his wet nappy to tell her that he has wet himself and might even sit on the potty (if the time is right). But he might also refuse to do so and should not be pressed (see toilet training, p. 104). At this age the infant finds his playpen rather cramped and he will throw all his toys out. He can even throw them quite far now. There is nothing wrong with doing this according to Gesell: 'it requires a fairly advanced development of the nervous cells. This is why the infant spends quite a considerable period of time in learning how to throw properly as it is an exercise which demands practice.' He also adores throwing a ball back to someone and he manages to throw it back with a sharp, jerky movement of the arm which makes him fall over.

'Towards the age of 15 months the child stops being a baby but he still has a great deal of progress still to make.'

Games

— balls, spoons, cups, toys which can be taken apart, fitted one into the other, etc.
— children's records
— a rocking horse
— pencils and paper
— sturdy picture books
— cubes
— ring pyramids and beakers which fit one into another.

Fig. 2.49 15 months: the infant often puts his spoon into his mouth upside down.

18 MONTHS

Postures

— He can climb the stairs (held by the hand) at 18 months.
— He can climb downstairs (held by the hand) at 21 months (Fig. 2.50).
— He can bend down to pick something up (Fig. 2.51).
— He starts to jump on both feet.
— He runs (with his legs apart) and often falls.
— He can pull a toy behind him (Fig. 2.52).
— He can walk backwards.

The use of the hands

— He can throw a ball (without falling).
— He can push a ball along with his foot (without falling).
— He can take off his shoes (if they do not have laces) and all his clothes provided that they do not have buttons or zip fastenings.
— He can eat by himself (fairly) cleanly (turning the spoon the right way up inside his mouth).
— He likes scribbling (see children's drawings, p. 88).

Understanding

— He is interested in picture books and can point out one or two pictures (i.e. dog and cat).
— He can say the word for one or two everyday objects.
— He can point to two or three parts of his body (for example, eyes, nose, mouth).
— He can understand one or two orders* and carries them out.
— He can control his bowels (during the day) although there may be some lapses (see chapter on toilet training, p. 100).
— *Building games*: he can make towers of three to four cubes.

*Example: Go and fetch the cat, put it on the chair.

Fig. 2.50 Around the age of 21 months the infant can go downstairs if his hand is held.

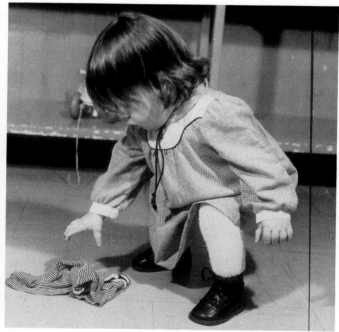

Fig. 2.51 18 months: the infant bends down to pick up an object.

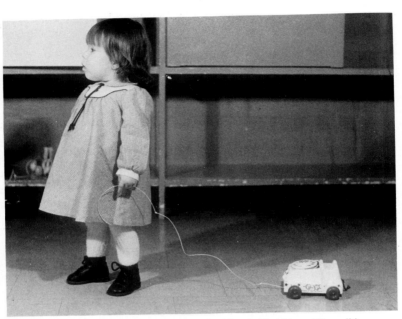

Fig. 2.52 18 months: the child can 'pull' an object behind him while walking.

— *Posting boxes*: he can fit two or three blocks into the board.

Language

The baby still uses 'general meaningful language' the same as when he was 15 months old (p. 57). He orders his words according to how important they are to him and he often puts himself first. The infant often uses language in order to join in with what adults are doing or to attract attention. He will become extremely voluble whenever his parents have visitors and will even go as far as to stop the conversation or drown it out. He should be listened to but he must also learn to be quiet. From now on he has got to learn that if one is to speak one must first of all learn to listen. He still finds it hard to hold a dialogue. His family can encourage (and even accelerate) verbal progress but never to a greater extent than his natural development will allow. What is most important is to remember to speak and reply to the child at his own level. It has been observed that orphan babies who live in an orphanage are unable to communicate as they have not had a family to stimulate them. These children felt that nobody was interested in them and they therefore felt no desire to speak. Also, a recent survey in the U.S.A has shown that children with behavioural problems are, in the majority of cases, the children of intellectual parents who are very demanding as regards the type of language the child produces and who are unwilling to play childish games which they (wrongly) believe to be too 'simplistic'.

Parents should try not to feel embarassed about talking lovingly to their child because even if what they say does not provide ideal models of speech, they will help their child associate language with *affection between people* and this will stimulate his progress.

Christopher (18 months old)

The whole garden now seems too small to satisfy Christopher's thirst for discovery. He wants to explore its every corner. He runs, turns round and round, jumps up and down whenever he sees a flower (and probably jumps on it in his excitement) and he often falls. It is a good thing that his mother is at hand to pick him up and set him off again as he could go on for ever. He discovers three blocks of stone on his travels and wants a hand to climb them. He would like to continue playing but it is teatime. His

Mum asks him to go up to the terrace and fetch his napkin. Christopher does not obey immediately. His mother tells him off.

There are a few tears and he finally resigns himself to sitting down and eating his bread and butter (without making a mess). When he has finished his afternoon tea Christopher takes it upon himself to put away his (dirty) cup and spoon in the cupboard and he then goes off to fetch his picture book which he hands to his mother. He would really like her to show him the farm animals (he does not yet know them all). Unfortunately, Mum does not have the time to spend with him at the moment and gives him some toys. He spends some time carrying these from one side of the room to the other.

Social development

The infant is extremely *lively*. He is so keen on running that he will grasp the slightest opportunity to make an escape. He takes off into the garden, on to the balcony, into the corridor of the block of flats, on to the staircase (he adores climbing up and down the stairs but he still needs an adult to help him). If he has elder brothers or sisters who pretend to chase him he will squeal with delight. He still often falls or bumps into things as he rushes headlong. He has not yet learnt to run round corners. He has not quite mastered the upright position and he has to run with his legs slightly splayed to keep his balance and he sometimes uses his arms to balance. Despite this, he is quite fearless and seizes every opportunity to try out his new motor skills: by pushing a chair, pulling his little car behind him on a string, walking backwards, jumping up and down, crouching down and standing up again, playing with a ball (he can now throw it back to someone without falling over). This is a fairly turbulent time in the life of an infant. He does not now however get overexcited in the same way as he did previously. He can play quietly on his own for 30 to 40 minutes.

There are some games he particularly enjoys playing on his own: carrying toys from one side of the room to the other and repeating the same actions 10 or 20 times. This enables him to discover the space around him. This activity has a purpose according to Gesell[1]: 'In order to make discoveries and to find things out, the child needs to explore. If one wants to know where one has started out from, it is necessary to retrace one's steps and so this coming and going is a logical part of development.'

A child of this age also tends to put things back where they came from. According to Maria Montessori[4] 'one of the most important and mysterious stages of a child's development is when he acquires a sense of order. This may appear at any time after the child is 1 and is acquired before he is 2 years old.' The child is reassured by objects which are in their place as these provide him with landmarks and help him control his environment better. He notices if his face flannel has been moved and if a bar of soap is not in its container he will immediately put it back. The game of hide-and-seek where the child finds the person he is looking for always in the same place is part of the same process. Children will adore this game until the age of about 4 years and woe betide anyone who tries to hide properly!

Nevertheless the child is interested in intellectual activities and enjoys picture books although he is clumsy in handling them (as he still turns over several pages at a time). He can spend long periods looking at the picture of an animal he is familiar with, call it by its name and even talk to it for a while but he has a very short attention span and lives for the instant. For Gesell, one interesting feature in a child of this age is his interest in completed actions.[1] He likes to finish off what he is doing and to carry out an action precisely and in its entirety. He enjoys fetching his napkin and dish before sitting down to his meal and putting his plate or dish (which may still be dirty) away after use. He enjoys using his pot and then emptying it into the toilet (this marks the beginning of toilet training, see p. 100), and even his favourite words and expressions often refer to a completed action ('daddy gone', 'milk allgone', etc.). His satisfaction at being able to refer to a completed action can be read in his expression. At this age he understands perfectly one or two orders given by his mother (if they are clearly expressed) but he is not always very obedient. Words alone are not always effective unless the tone is somewhat sharpened! The child's relationship with other children of his own age is not, as yet, particularly harmonious. An 18 month-old child will push, pinch, bite and hit them as if they were 'toys'. He is not ready to play games with other children and will play by himself with his back turned to the other children.

Games

As for 15 months.

2 YEARS (24 MONTHS)

Postures

— He can climb up and down stairs unaided (he puts both feet on each step).
— He runs fast (he has a better sense of balance), can go round in a circle, skip up and down, climb and dance.
— He can kick a ball (accurately and without losing his balance) (Fig. 2.53).
— He can jump on both feet.
— He can bend over to pick something up (he bends slightly at the waist and knees).

The use of the hands

His wrists have become extremely supple and he can rotate his forearm and this accounts for the following developments:

— He can open and shut doors.
— He can wash his face and dry it unaided.
— He can put on his shoes on his own (he may occasionally put them on the wrong feet).
— He can put on a jacket or trousers (unless there are buttons or a zip fastener).
— He can leaf through a picture book page by page (Fig. 2.54).
— He enjoys scribbling and can copy lines made by an adult.

— He can now feed himself properly on his own (Fig. 2.55).

Understanding

— He can say what four or five pictures are.
— He can name four or five common objects.
— He can point to four or five parts of his body.
— He can understand two or three orders given at the same time.★
— He can control his bowels and is clean during the day.

★Example: Go and fetch the cat, put it in the kitchen give it its milk.

Fig. 2.53 2 years: the child can 'kick' a ball.

Fig. 2.54 2 years: the child enjoys leafing through a picture book page by page.

— He can control his bladder and is (generally) clean during the day. He can go to the toilet but he needs his mother to wipe him.
— *Construction games*: he can make towers of six to eight cubes.
— *Posting boxes*: he can fit four blocks into the board.
— *Jigsaw puzzles*: he can fit together three to four pieces.
— He knows one (or two) colours (and can place an object on something else of the same colour).
— He can count to three or four.

Language

This is generally the time when language acquisition gathers a blistering momentum. The infant uses 'verbs', he constructs 'explicit phrases' and he abandons his jargon (which has been mentioned previously). He may be able to 'construct sentences' but this does not mean to say that he will start to 'speak like a grown-up'. He will still use a kind of babytalk which his parents should not worry about. He might say 'Jack's teddy is beddibies' or 'Baby's going to eat cake.'

At this age he often refers to himself by his Christian name or by 'Baby'. (Some children do already say 'I'.) Claude Langevin[3] tells that a worried mother came to tell him of the language used by her child while making sand-castles. What the child had said was the following: 'Andrew's making big tower, take a block, put it here . . . Oh, all fall down! Andrew doesn't want block, it falls Mum.' He was able to reassure her that this language was correct for a child of this age. The child was using syntax and the verb and pronunciation and intonation were correct. Real 'babytalk' deforms language completely

What is worrying is when adults start to use this baby talk either because they find it amusing or because they think it helps them find the baby's own level and thus be more easily understood.

It is as dangerous to talk to the baby in a literary style as it is to indulge in babytalk with him!

Fig. 2.55 The child can *eat on his own* properly.

Emma (2 years old)

This little slip of a girl who weighs 12 kg is already a big sister as little Christopher made his appearance on the family scene just 2 weeks ago.

Emma was very upset by this and started to wet herself again several times a day. Her mother understood what was at the root of the problem and made sure that she got more attention. Emma, who was being called 'a big girl now', demanded lots of cuddles and even started to want her bottle again.

This big baby now likes to potter tirelessly around the flat, often climbing on the furniture and even wanting to get up to the sink. She likes the washing up bowl because she can dip her fingers in the water and pretend to be doing the housework. Her mother would rather that she played with her children's games (for example, Plasticine, cubes, picture books and painting). But she usually likes playing with her doll best of all! In the evening she puts on its nightie and takes it to bed with her. She refuses to go to sleep without her doll. Sometimes she also calls for her teddy or her pot and it takes her some time to get to sleep as she often calls for her mother on some pretext or other.

Social development

A 2-year-old infant is half-way

between being a baby and being a child. His parents are often disconcerted by both the progress he has made and the number of things he is still unable to do.

He appears to be so capable and sociable, playing a full role within the family and helping his mother with certain household tasks that it is easy to give him too much freedom and act as though he were already grown up. At this age a continual watch should be kept on him as his sheer exuberance can lead him into doing the worst possible things such as climbing on to a windowsill, putting a plastic bag over his head or falling headlong down the stairs. His motor co-ordination has improved and he can now run fast and in the direction he wants (he no longer rushes straight ahead as he did at 18 months and therefore does not fall so frequently). He skips, turns in circles and likes activities which have rhythm (songs which he can clap his hands to and tap his feet to).

A 2-year-old child is not only attracted to games which allow him to practise his motor development but he also enjoys games which require thought and manipulation such as posting boxes, simple jigsaws and simple building games: he can put six to eight building blocks together and bring what he has made to life (it is amusing to eavesdrop on his long conversations when he is playing on his own). He enjoys putting objects into containers and then taking them out again (he particularly enjoys games which involve a cardboard or any other kind of box). He enjoys natural raw materials, particularly sand and water, and hollows the sand into troughs which he fills up with water. If there is no sandpit available he can be given modelling

clay (or even flour and water) to play with.

Bathtime is an especially good time for a variety of 'watersports' and even during the day the child enjoys washing his hands (he might spend long periods of time emptying and filling the basin, dipping his hands in the water, soaping them, rinsing them and playing with the

water. At this age the bathroom holds an especial attraction for him).

Sometimes a 2-year-old can be extremely demanding at home whilst being very reserved at nursery school. He is going through a stage when he is shy with people that he does not know and when he is very attached to his mother. The reactions of children of this age to

Fig. 2.56 2 years: the child is extremely *possessive*.

nursery school may vary (see p. 82). The infant prefers playing on his own to playing with other people. He has not yet learnt how to co-operate with others and when he is with other children he watches them but is not yet ready to play with them. The infant is extremely possessive about his toys (Fig. 2.56) and will clasp them to his chest if there is even the remotest possibility that he might have to share them! This kind of behaviour is normal as the child has to learn what it is to have things of his own before he can learn to share them. The nursery nurse or the child's mother could already start to introduce him to playing with others by asking him to find a toy for his little friend 'You've got the ball . . . now what can we find for Peter? Go and find him a car.' One should not be surprised if the sight of another child inspires him to kicking, pushing, hair-pulling or, for no apparent reason, smothering the other child with affection by tightly hugging and kissing him!

Games between children of this age frequently end in tears.

A 2-year-old child is at a 'cross-roads' and this is a difficult time for his parents. This is generally considered to be the time when the child is most frequently slapped, which is perhaps not the most appropriate solution. The child understands what he is told and if he can be 'taken in hand' and talked to firmly but kindly he may indeed learn self-discipline and become very sociable. The parents will nonetheless have to put up with their child being 'diffi-cult' for some months yet. At meal-times he will point to what he wants to eat. He can feed himself (although he is sometimes rather messy) and if his mother tries to feed him he will dismiss her peremp-torily. He wants to do it 'by himself'! His family will find his bossiness wearing: he may tell his family where they each have to sit round the meal table. His sense of order is at its peak (see p. 61) and he knows where all the furniture ought to be and also the order in which all family rituals should be carried out and so woe betide anyone who steps out of line.

He finds it difficult to get to sleep at night: he has to go through certain rituals before being put to bed like fetching his teddy or his doll, having the door left open, the lights left on in the corridor and a glass of water by his bed. His imag-ination knows no bounds when it comes to dreaming up a pretext on which to call his mother. This very childish behaviour will start to disappear as he approaches the age of 3 years.

Games

— storybooks, picture books, post cards
— string, marbles, boxes, swings
— modelling clay, sand games (bucket and spade), games which involve fitting objects into each other and separating them again, taking things apart and putting them together again
— paints, crayons, paper, easy jigsaws, posting boxes
— rocking horse, pulling toys, pushing toys
— toys which move: cars, trains, tricycles, swings
— children's records (songs with rhythm)
— imitation games (for example, a housewife's outfit, doll's house, bear, dolls). These will be essen-tial for when he is 3 years old.

3 YEARS (36 MONTHS)

Postures

His sense of balance is now complete

— He can climb up and down stairs like an adult.
— He can jump down from the last step of the stairs (for fun).
— He can jump on one leg and keep his balance on one foot for several seconds (if asked to do so).
— He can ride his little tricycle.
— He can walk like an adult (swinging his arms alternately).

Use of the hands

— He can dress himself (and can often cope with buttons and zip fasteners).
— He can put on his shoes (when he is 4 years old he will be able to do up the laces).
— He can help to clear the table (without breaking anything).
— He can draw a circle (a little man, see p. 89) (Fig. 2.57).

Understanding

— He can say what six to eight pictures are.
— He can name six to eight everyday objects.
— He can point to six to eight parts of the body.
— He can carry out three to four orders given consecutively*.
— He can control his bowels and his bladder (he is toilet trained. See special chapter p. 100).

*Example: Go and fetch the cat, put it in the kitchen, give it something to drink, stay with it.

— *Construction games*: he can build a tower of eight to nine blocks and make a bridge with the blocks (if an adult shows him how) (Fig. 2.58).

— *Posting boxes*: he can fit all the shapes into the board (Fig. 2.59).

— He knows some children's songs.

— He knows three to four colours (and match colours).

— He can count up to six or eight (and sometimes even to ten).

Language

A 3-year-old should now be able to talk (he should be able to produce all his consonants and vowels without confusion or substituting one for another). By this age, if the child has any difficulties in making himself understood these should be treated as grounds for concern.

His *vocabulary* increases by leaps and bounds, he swamps his parents with *questions* and it is impossible to quench his thirst for new words.

He tends to be egocentric and uses 'I' and 'me' in a lot of what he says (previously he referred to himself by his Christian name or as 'baby').

Nonetheless, learning a language is not easy and any little mistakes he does makes should not be frowned upon. There is no point in accusingly picking him up on what he has

Fig. 2.57 3 years: the child can draw a 'balloon man'.

Fig. 2.58 3 years: the child can build a tower of 8 to 9 cubes.

said and pointing out his mistakes in syntax. It is much better if he has a good example to follow. If he is provided with examples, progress will lead on of its own accord. If, however, an opportunity arises to substitute the correct word for what the baby has said wrong it should be grasped. The child is also a perfectionist and if he is treated with tact he will be only too happy to give of his best. He could be introduced to little vocal games of the type suggested by Claude Langevine[3] which will increase his repertoire and improve his language.

For example

— Putting a finger under his nose so that he can feel what making an 'm' sound is like.
— Playing at being an 'angry cat' in front of a mirror (he puts his upper teeth over his lower lip and makes 'fff').
— Showing him what your tongue does when you pass from one letter to another and trying to help him, in front of the mirror, correct any little speech difficulties he might have.
— Playing guessing games: John's gone to fetch his slip . . . (pers), his tow . . . (el) etc.
— Imitating rather special everyday sounds: the air being let out of a balloon, the song of a bird, the noise of a train, etc.
— Using little picture or children's story books, and records with animal calls which he can imitate.

When playing these games, parents should endeavour not to interrupt the child continually to point out his mistakes but rather try to create a happy, relaxed atmosphere so that the child enjoys these activities. If the child does not succeed in what is wanted of him he should not be pressed. He will learn correct pronunciation in his own time just as he learnt to talk in the first place.

Ethel (3 years old)

Mrs D. is happily watching her little girl Ethel who is putting away the groceries in the cupboard with particular care and attention. 'Well done, you're a big girl now,' says her Mum. Ethel adores her mother's company, gazes at her full of admiration, likes seeing her all made up and asks if she can try some nail varnish too. Her mother often says no and this upsets Ethel. Yesterday, when her mother was out, Ethel went into the bedroom and got out the nail varnish. But, unfortunately, she dropped it. When her mother came home she shouted at Ethel who thankfully had her father to run to. Her Dad stood up for her and said that 'nothing disastrous had happened'. Ethel was rather upset by the whole affair and shouted that her mother was 'nasty' and 'horrible' and then she went and gave her father a big cuddle and told

Fig. 2.59 3 years: the child can fit all the shapes into his 'posting box'.

him 'Daddy, darling I love you and want to stay with you. Will you marry me when I'm grown up?' Her father, caught off balance a little by this sudden question, fobbed her off with 'Yes, darling, but now run along and look after your own little girl. She's waiting for you.' Ethel went and comforted herself with her doll as only this little rag person seemed to understand her. She got out an (empty) pot of nail varnish and she mimed the whole episode. She and her doll had a long chat together.

Social development

According to Gesell 'the child reaches a kind of age of majority at 3 years', it is the age when he is adorable. All the excesses, paradoxes and troubles of the previous months give way to a greater degree of maturity. The child seems more sensible and sure of himself and this is the ideal time for him to start nursery school (see p. 81). He has an excellent sense of balance. He is perfectly able to control all his movements and adopt any position. It is the way he can now use his hands which opens the door to independence for him: he can dress himself, put on his shoes, help with the housework, draw and eat without making a mess.

He can control his bladder and bowels, be clean for 24 hours a day and go to the toilet by himself. His intellect has surged ahead over recent months: he can talk properly and easily make himself understood and his thirst for knowledge can be seen from the questions he keeps firing at his parents. 'Why?' is one of the most frequently used words at this age. He starts to think about others, to listen to what adults say and to learn more. He has become more sociable and appreciates the company of others better. He has started to learn how to wait his turn but he is only beginning to learn

how to get on with a group and generally prefers to be left playing on his own. In spite of this he does appreciate the company of others and enjoys the company of his class-mates, visits to friends' houses and birthdays.

He likes games which require some thought: 'jigsaw puzzles', 'building games', 'posting boxes', etc . . . He knows colours, can count, can draw a figure, he enjoys listening to records more, being told stories and reading picture books (with Dad!).

In the evening he goes to bed just like a grown up and needs fewer rituals before going to sleep. It is not surprising to hear him during the night; he might get up to go to the toilet, to get a biscuit or even to read a picture book! Some anxious chil-dren will want to go and climb into their parents' bed, often on the pretext of a nightmare (which they will find very hard to explain). At this age, if the child gets up for a walk and finds that his parents are out he might get very upset. He will cry and not be able to understand why they are not there. If the baby sitter is known to the child it might be easy to comfort him. The child should always be warned in advance if the parents are going out as he is quite capable of understanding this. It is preferable for him to know the babysitter (parents should imagine how worried they would be if they woke up to find their family gone and a stranger in the house!). Parents should make an effort to understand what is going on in the child's mind. A child who cries at night and wants to get into his parents' bed is often seeking affec-tion and security. Going to nursery school and meeting new people is upsetting for the child and he needs

the security of his family. Gesell believes that a great deal of under-standing is needed at this time. 'It is better', he says, 'to give in to the child on the firm understanding that once he is asleep he will be put back in his own bed'.[1] He is not going to go to his parents with this demand for very long and so there is no reason why he should be refused this 'comfort'.

A play world

A child who does not go to school may play for hours at length on his own in his bedroom with his favourite toys. This is the age for *make-believe* (see p. 98) (Fig. 2.60) and he holds long conversations with his teddy or his doll and acts out scenes from adult life. He may even invent an 'imaginary friend' (who has his own seat at table, in the car, etc.). His power of '*animism*' enables him to bring things to life (if the child bumps into the wardrobe he might smack it and tell it that it is naughty!). Parents should not encourage the child in this but neither should they ever mock these flights of fancy. When the child grows older he will learn to adapt to the adult world and no longer need to take refuge in make-believe. A 3-year-old child is very active and enjoys playing outside: on tobog-gans, swings, with a ball. This will help him expend some of his energy and learn the rules of playing with other people. The child finds it difficult to acquire self-discipline and has not yet learnt to wait his turn. When he is playing ball he would like to be the one who is throwing the ball and the one who is catching it at the same time. He does want to play with others but he finds it hard not to be self-centred.

Fig. 2.60 3 years is the age for 'make-believe'.

Likewise, if he sees a friend building a sand-castle beside him he immediately wants his friend's bucket and spade (even if he has one of his own in front of him). This rather awkward attitude is typical of the psychology of a child of this age and shows a real desire to co-operate which the child has not yet learnt to put into practice. He does not want to take anything away from anybody, he wants to become 'the other person who is playing'. He will not really start to collaborate with other children until he is 6 years old. In the meantime, his parents and teachers have a whole series of rows, fights and tears to contend with!

The notion of right and wrong

At this age the child is able to under-stand what is 'allowed' and what is 'not allowed' and this forms the basis for his moral upbringing. When a child hears his mother say 'no' he knows that he has done something wrong and he knows how wrong it is by the tone of her voice. This is why parents should maintain a *scale of values* (for example, a child should receive a more severe telling off for biting his brother than for breaking a glass). Also the parents should be *consistent* in their demands (yesterday when Robert pulled Anne's hair, his mother did not scold him whereas today she was furious), and also *firm* (Sophy took a cake out of the cupboard, her mother scolded her, she started to cry and her mother, taking pity on her, decided to let her have it. What conclusion is the child to draw from

this?). Parents should also come to a common agreement over what they are and are not going to allow because if the child is allowed to do certain things by one parent but not by the other he will become very confused. The child expects the adult to impose discipline as he needs to be protected against the outside world and also against himself. He would find a lack of discipline utterly confusing although parents should be aware of how even the best of intentions can be easily sabotaged. Parents should take responsibility for their child's upbringing as children are not born with an innate sense of right and wrong: it is the adult who, through approving or disapproving of certain actions, determines the rules of behaviour. In the mind of a 3-year-old what is right is what pleases his mother and what is wrong is what displeases her. This is how the child develops a *conscience*. So parents must rise to the occasion. By the age of 4 years the child will have internalised his parent's code of conduct and this will form the basis of what the psychoanalysts call the '*superego*' which is indelibly imprinted on the child's unconscious.

Personality crisis

At 3 years the child undergoes a severe personality crisis which becomes apparent in a number of different ways and to a greater or lesser extent depending on the individual child.

Sexuality

A 3-year-old is confident about which sex he is and is perfectly capable of differentiating between men and women. In the course of family life he has become aware of the great differences in behaviour, dress, speech and also urination. It is the latter which prompts his initial discovery of the differences between the sexes. The child is particularly interested in the human body and frequently talks about the genital organs (see p. 105). Many of the questions he asks are about sex, motherhood and babies. Parents are often taken aback by these questions and are too embarrassed to reply. Nonetheless, there is very little depth to the child's questions; as the child's curiosity is limited all he is looking for is a simple answer (which is meaningful in his eyes if not necessarily in his parents' according to Gesell). The child's discovery of sexuality occasions a certain amount of tension in the

'parent-child' relationship. This is what is called the '*Oedipus phase*' (see section on sexuality, p. 109). The child discovers that he is alone and is a separate person from his parents who form a couple. Thus he has to adapt from a one-to-one relationship (he and his mother) to a triangular relationship (father-mother-child). In these circumstances, the child tries to find out where he fits in and in his attempts to gain recognition he tends mainly to seek the affection of the parent of the opposite sex and to reject the parent of the same sex. The child's behaviour changes. He becomes aggressive towards one of his two parents and goes through a difficult period. The way he manages to come to terms with this complex will depend to a large extent on how understanding his parents are. It is particularly important for him to manage to identify with his parents. The ability of the little boy to become detached from his mother has a great deal to do with his desire to be like his father. Likewise, the little girl's ability to detach herself from her father is connected with her desire to resemble her mother. She will try to copy her mother's gestures, tone of voice and behaviour. She will play at being the little woman and will want a husband. This kind of imitation is, in itself, a very positive attitude as the boy will tend towards masculinity and the girl towards femininity. The child will only be able to reach these goals if he really loves and admires his parents.

It is perfectly natural for parents to be delighted at this but they should not over-encourage their children to imitate them. A 3-year-old girl imitating her mother over the telephone is delightful but an infant dressed up just a miniature of his

parents can (sometimes) look a little ridiculous. Parents should remember that it is right and proper to guide and provide an example for one's children but they should also allow the child to develop his own personality.

Narcissism

The child is now much more aware of what he is capable of doing and of his own personality and he often talks of 'I' and 'me' and tends to believe that the world revolves around him. It is his mother's approval or disapproval which acts as a spur to his development. He is happiest when his mother is watching him doing something and 'Mummy, look!' is perhaps the phrase which is repeated the most in the life of a 3-year-old. The child piles achievement on achievement, receives compliment after compliment and grows in confidence daily. He becomes more independent and more alert. However, his actions may not be as straightforward as they seem as he often seeks to define his own personality through challenging the adult. He is permanently defiant and says 'no' in order to provoke his parents. The instant the child learns to do something new he will refuse any help whatsoever. He does not care if he is not properly washed or if his hair has hardly been brushed, what is important is that he has done it all by himself. Parents are too ready to rush to their child's assistance and treat him almost as though he were disabled. They are irritated by his slowness and clumsiness. It is hardly surprising that this attitude should infuriate the child, as he is at the stage when he wants everyone to recognize him as an individual. A child who is perpetually being helped and being told 'Come here, you can't manage that yet' will remain clumsy and lack assurance. A survey carried out by Rose Vincent[4] carried out on 200 children between the ages of 3 and 4 years has cast a great deal of light on this subject. The child was shown eight photographs of mothers and their children in a variety of typical situations. The mother who proved by far the most popular was the *mother friend*: the mother who remained in the background and sought the child's help. The *overprotective mother* was totally rejected by the majority of children. This shows how important the attitude, gestures and words, in short the image of the mother, is in the eyes of the child.

By watching, listening to and imitating his parents the child is building up the adult which one day he will become. So children should see the example of happy, well-balanced parents who help him to develop his own personality and most importantly move away from his parents to other people who may be less gentle and less kind but who will lead him towards becoming a 'social human being'.

REFERENCES

1 Gesell A 1980 Le jeune enfant dans la civilisation moderne. P.U.F., Paris
2 Freud A 1968 Normality and pathology in childhood. Hogarth Press, London
3 Langevin C 1970 Le langage de votre enfant. (de l'Homme ed.)
4 Montessori M 1970 L'enfant. Desclée De Brouwer, Paris
5 Bettleheim B 1980 Empty fortress. Free Press, US

Chapter 3
THE MAJOR STAGES OF SOCIALISATION

Types of care

GRANDPARENTS

Formerly children were brought up within an extended family made up of their grandparents and parents and it was often the grandparents who were responsible for bringing up the children. There was recognition of the experience they had gained with age and their authority in these matters went unchallenged. Families respected a natural hierarchy based on the traditions of previous generations. Nowadays modern life has led to people living apart more and when there is a family gathering the grandparents have to exercise discretion especially in as far as the upbringing of their grandchildren is concerned.

While it is universally recognised that the parents are the best people to care for and in particular to bring

their children up it is equally true that the grandparents can be of invaluable assistance to them and that their support is of benefit to the child. However grandparents need to be skilful in tackling their role as it is never an easy one. They need to display a great deal of tact and understanding as it is not easy to give advice without it sounding like a command, to help without taking over completely, to remain in the background, to give one's opinion briefly without imposing it, to play an active role while remaining on the sidelines, in short, to act as a 'cushion'[1].

Grandparents should make an effort to understand the young parents, to become more tolerant and broad-minded while the young parents should teach their children what it is to be part of a family, to know that there are people who have

come before as there will be those who come after and to appreciate the sense of continuity that being part of a family brings.

It has been shown that today's children show a great deal of nostalgia for the idea of the traditional family. The results of a survey of 800 young people (from nursery school to the sixth form) are proof in themselves: all love their grandparents, want to see them more often or live nearer to them. The youngest gave reasons such as 'Granny makes cakes', 'Grandpa tells me stories, makes things with me, gardens.' At the age of 12 years, the child associates his grandparents with holidays and outings. At 16 years the young people often find it hard to accept their grandparents' criticism or their quiet routine lifestyle. Nonetheless, young people seem to find that their grandparents

Fig. 3.1

are the easiest people to confide in and the simple fact that they can have a second family adds to their sense of security.

Through two very different situations it is possible to analyse the positive and negative aspects of the 'three-way-relationship' between children, grandparents and parents.

Case studies

On Wednesday, Richard (3) visited his grandparents who live in a house in the country. Richard spent the whole day following them everywhere, happily listening to his grandmother telling him stories or following his grandfather out into the garden where he helped him to pick some vegetables and to plant some flowers.

When Mum came to fetch him Richard did not look very happy to see her. He even asked to stay at his grandparents'. His mother got cross and tried to drag him away whereupon he burst into tears and to try and comfort him his grandmother promised him that if he was good he could come back again the next Wednesday.

Grandmother has been living at the young parents' home since Virginia (4) was born and looks after her while her mother works.

Today it is time for the family meal and Virginia does not look very hungry. Her mother scolds her and Virginia asks her grandmother to spoonfeed her. 'You're not a baby any longer, eat it up by yourself!' her mother snaps. Virginia refuses point blank to eat and puts her elbows on the table! This really sparks off her mother's anger and she scolds Virginia about her manners. Grandmother rises from the table with a worried look on her face and tells her daughter that she should not be treating her child like that, that she never has any problems with Virginia.

Table 3.1A

Positive attitudes of grandparents	Results on small child
The grandparents are of 'assistance' to the parents and can stand in for them and help to mind the children.	This form of child-minding gives the child a great sense of security as he knows his grandparents.
They offer a different *lifestyle*: a different home, a change of furniture, habits and ways of doing things.	This helps the child to socalise.
They can give the parents 'advice' based on common sense and personal experience.	The child benefits.
They have more free time than the parents and therefore: — have the time to listen to the child — have the time to talk to the child — have the time to tell him stories.	Develops the child's intelligence, imagination and builds self-esteem and a sense of security.
They can offer extra affection.	An emotionally balanced child.
They can make helpful comparisons about two ways of doing something: 'That's what your parents do'. 'That's also what I used to do'. 'It's perhaps the best way.'	Develops the child's critical faculties.
They have a quieter lifestyle than the parents.	Has a calming effect.
They support the parents in bringing up the child.	Helps the child develop a conscience and learn to obey rules (helps socialisation).
They act as a *'cushion'* (when the child is upset they 'comfort' him and try to explain to him what he has done wrong.	Provides a calm atmosphere.
A good relationship between parents and grandparents (a friendly, affectionate exchange of ideas).	A well-balanced child as he lives in a happy, stimulating environment. Concept of family.
The grandparents talk to the child about his parents 'when they were little'.	Sense of time and of the continuity of life.
Calm, relaxed grandparents.	Presents old age in a good light.

Table 3.1B

Negative attitudes of grandparents	Results on the young child
The grandparents take over from the parents and 'stand in for them' (this is generally observed when they look after the child full-time).	The child will have several parental images (which may cause him psychological problems).
They *criticise* the parents in front of the child.	Diminishes the parents' prestige and authority.
They are 'disciplinarian' and order the parents about in front of the child.	Poor socialisation of the child.
They are *'overprotective'* and protect the child regardless of what he has done.	Promotes tantrums and blackmail.
They do not want him to be scolded and try to protect him from everything.	
They 'spoil' the child (cakes, sweets etc.).	Hinders upbringing and socialisation and is bad for health. Develops a sense of guilt.
They exercise 'emotional blackmail' (e.g. 'Stay with me and I'll give you sweets' etc. They make every attempt to win the child's affection.	Bad moral education (promotes the idea of self-interest).
They insist on 'different standards' from those of the parents, 'You can leave your elbows on the table, your mother's not here!' etc.	Upsets the child's upbringing and creates feelings of guilt.
Rows between grandparents and parents.	Creates an atmosphere of tension which is harmful to the child.
Jealousy of grandmother and mother for each other.	Makes the child nervous and upset!

CHILDMINDERS, NURSERIES AND PLAYGROUPS

GENERAL REMARKS

The personality of the individual is developed over the early years of his or her life.

Heredity does play an important role but everything ultimately hinges on the experiences and the relationships enjoyed by the young child. 'The dice are cast by the age of 3' according to Freud. Every effort should therefore be made to ensure that the child has a happy and secure environment over these particularly critical years of his life. We already know to what extent the young child needs the same people, surroundings and care for his wellbeing. Parents should also look to their child's intellectual and social future and strive for the best ways to stimulate

him and answer his needs at particular stages in his development.

Child care is therefore of major concern to those parents who are aware of their own responsibility in this matter.

The number of women who work outside the home is on the increase. Changes in family structure and life-style and the desire of women to play a more active role in the economic life of the country have obliged the authorities to consider the best ways of caring for the very young child. If the mother decides to work she should find someone to look after her child in the initial months (before the child becomes too attached to her) or after he is 15 months old since a child between the ages of 8 and 15 months is going through a critical period where separation is not desirable (see p. 42) on the crisis of anxiety during the 8th month).

The mother is warmly recommended to care for the child herself for the first year. She needs to be happy about taking on this maternal duty and be financially able to devote herself to her child. Nowadays it is those women who could most easily give up work who show the least desire to look after their child. Some women are seeking to climb the social ladder and are looking for self-fulfilment in their work! It is a very sorry thing that motherhood should be so under-valued and it is time that mothers became aware of how important their role really is. Nowadays there are a number of measures which enable the mother to look after her child for the first year and to compensate her loss of salary.

Next comes the problem of choosing the right type of child care and every effort should be made for the child's upbringing to fit in well with the mother's need to work. Is this need to work to the detriment of the child or is it perhaps to his benefit? There are a variety of types of child care which can be adapted to family circumstances and to whether both parents work all day or not. The important thing is that the care of the child should not come between him and either of his parents. The traditional stereotype of the grandmother who looks after the child is far from being a thing of the past and nowadays young parents are expressing an even greater need for them. However, this form of child care is not open to everyone and sometimes it causes problems which are better avoided (see p. 74). The choice will therefore be between the 'childminder' and the 'nursery' or 'playgroup'. There are pros and cons on both sides which need to be examined carefully as it is not

Fig. 3.2

merely a question of finding somewhere to leave the baby but rather to find somewhere where he can grow and develop.

The registered childminder looks after other people's children under the age of 5 years in her own home for more than 2 hours per day up to 6 days. The childminder is registered with the local authority social services department. The Department of Health and Social Security does issue guidelines for minimum standards but these are not statutory. The local authority, however, may impose certain requirements, e.g. childminders must be under retirement age, keep a daily register of attendance and complete a declaration of health.

Local authority nurseries also take in young children as do private nurseries run by charities, businesses or colleges. Nurseries which usually open from early morning to early evening enable mothers to leave their children during working hours. A proportion of staff is trained in the care of the under-5s. All groups of young children (premises or person-in-charge) must be registered with the local authority social services department under the Nursery and Child Minders Act, 1958.

In a report on working women and nurseries in France Dr Françoise Davidson[2] presented the results of a survey of 200 young women who were asked what type of child care they would select if they were unable to obtain any help from the 'grandparents'. The result was that most preferred the nursery to placing their child with a family as they found that the advantages of the nursery outweighed its disadvantages.

Mothers are aware that if they hand their child over to an establishment it is unlikely that their child will become very attached to any person in particular. The mother can therefore retain a central role in her child's life.

In Table 3.3 on page 80 there is an analysis of the two types of child care most commonly used by mothers. Each has advantages and disadvantages which the mother should study carefully before making any decision. It should perhaps be pointed out that while every effort has been made to improve the standards of hygiene and education provided by both nurseries and childminders there is considerable progress still to be made before the child can be assured of a climate which is favourable to his psychomotor development.

In the nursery the child helpers should become more flexible in their attitudes towards their work and try to avoid, in so far as is possible, falling into routines which can only be of detriment to human relationships. Childminders (where the child is placed with a family) should also be made more aware of child psychology. Their home often provides a drab, routine existence which retards both the child's intellectual development and his socialisation.

Parents should, in any case, resist the temptation of rushing to hasty conclusions about the various types of child care available based on personal prejudice. While it is true that there are some nurseries where the play room is a sorry spectacle (either because so little is provided or because the staff are unwilling to make any effort) there are some cases where the childminder has made every effort to meet the child's needs fully. The case studies which follow should give an idea of what can be expected but are not intended to be a systematic study. Some rather extreme examples have been chosen intentionally to provide food for thought.

THE CHILDMINDER

Part-time care by a childminder

Case study

Natalie is 2. When she was 1 year old she was sent to a childminder not far from the family home. Her mother fetches her in the evening to bring her home for the family meal and also brings her home on Wednesdays and for the entire weekend. The minder talks to Natalie often, tells her stories, takes her out for walks or takes her to collect her own children from school. Natalie is a happy child who enjoys running about and playing with the other children; she is articulate and very affectionate towards her minder. When her mother comes to collect her she makes no fuss about leaving. Natalie says a nice goodbye to her minder and never throws a tantrum.

Explanation

This child was not too young when she was sent to a childminder: her mother was able to look after her for the first year of her life (and it is during this period that the strongest bonds are formed).

Natalie found it easy to come to terms with this separation from her mother as this was only for part of the time.

The child accepted her minder easily as the minder displayed a number of invaluable maternal qualities and, what is more, the presence of other children in the home turned out to be a stimulus for her.

The positive features of this placement are apparent. The child's psycho-motor development is completely normal and she finds it easy to accept the daily separation.

Full-time placement with a childminder

Case study

When she was 2 months old Valerie was sent to a childminder, Mrs X. in the provinces. Her mother, Mrs Wares, had chosen this solution as she was very busy and her accommodation was unsuitable. She remained attached to her little girl but only managed to visit her on the occasional weekend. Valerie was unwilling to go to her mother and cried a lot. Now Valerie is 3 years old and her mother has just taken her back and sent her to nursery school. Valerie is now aggressive towards her classmates and her teachers and occasionally spends long periods on her own staring into space. She refuses to eat in the evening and often wakes up in tears and asks her mother if she can go back to Mrs X.

Explanation

This child displays the typical symptoms of 'psychological distress' due to being suddenly separated from her minder. The child had; in effect; focused all her affections on the one person who had cared for her since she was 2 months old. She feels that somehow, inexplicably, she has been abandoned by her minder.

Valerie has two 'mother images': that of her minder who she sees as her real mother (as she has lavished care and affection on her) and that of a stranger who 'says that she is her mother' (she does not understand why this person is there or what she is there for). This is why she feels upset and insecure and shows this by aggression, anorexia and bad nights.

This kind of placement has extremely deleterious effects. The child has not seen her real mother often enough to be able to understand the situation and has become excessively attached to the person who is looking after her.

Furthermore, a sudden transfer to a nursery school does not help matters. The child feels all the more at sea and cannot settle down at school under these circumstances.

Table 3.2 Problems raised by placement with a childminder

Relationship child-childminder	Relationship child-mother	Relationship mother-childminder
The child becomes too attached to the childminder: — because the minder is too fond of him — devotes too much time to him — cannot have children of her own — no longer has any children — is able to devote herself exclusively to him and spoils him.	*The child may prefer the minder*: This leads to conflict with the mother and the child becomes aggressive, anorexic and has nightmares. Contributory factors: — his mother is unavailable — he feels he has been abandoned or rejected — he is sent to nursery school without a transition period.	The mother and the childminder should agree on: — education — nutrition — when the child is to be brought and collected The child needs a routine and likes to feel that these two people who are 'dear' to him see eye to eye.
The child does not become attached to the childminder: — because the minder lacks motivation — is too old — is insensitive or hard — has too many children to look after or prefers her own — he changes minder frequently.	*The child needs to know who his mother is*: He should not have two 'mother images'. *Mutual affection should be reinforced by frequent, happy contact* The mother should ensure that there is continuity in the child's — education — nutrition — environment etc.	*The mother and the minder should be mutually supportive.* Each should talk to the child about the other with respect and friendship. *The mother and the childminder should retain their respective roles.* The childminder should not take over from the mother and the mother should be responsible for her child.
Excessive attachment to the minder should be avoided: (the child should be taught to make the difference). *The minder should be advised to provide the child with*: — affection — security.		

Fig. 3.3 'The problem of individualising methods of feeding is as difficult as that of finding individual ways of helping each child to sleep. The problem must be faced.' (Irene Lezine).

Fig. 3.4 A model nursery is not one where the child puts on the most weight but where he is the happiest. (Professor Lelong).

Fig. 3.5 'The nursery teaches the child to socialise' (Dr Vincent).

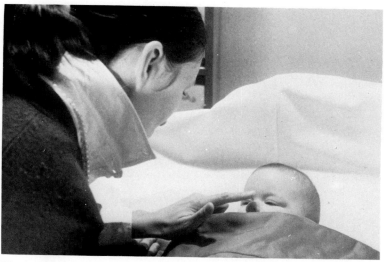

Fig. 3.6 'The attitude of the nurse towards the child and the nice things she finds to say to him help him accept the fact that it is time to take a nap.' (Irene Lezine).

Table 3.3 Comparison between two forms of child care: nursery and childminder (Part-time placement)

	Advantages	Disadvantages

Care by childminder	— frequent contact with the mother
	— (special times of the day have been preserved)
	— a flexible timetable (the mother can collect the child as and when she wishes)
	— pace of living is adapted to the personality of the child
	— the same person and environment (gives security)
	— a family atmosphere (gives security)
	— the child is taken when he is ill
	— greater affection is (often) shown than at the nursery (the minder is a good *'substitute mother'*)
	— if the mother has to go away for a few days the minder can look after the child
	— the minder keeps the mother informed about the child's progress (there is a good relationship)
		It is difficult to supervise childminders: some are not registered with the Local Authority and might not have the *qualities* required to look after a young child:
		— lack of hygiene
		— lack of motivation
		— lack of commitment
		— the childminder is too old
		— she is unqualified to provide:
		  education
		  nutrition
		  hygiene
		— the absence of other children in the home and a lack of stimulation could retard the child's progress
		— if there are too many children they cannot be properly supervised
		— more expensive than the nursery
		— (sometimes) rivalry between mother and minder which can be prejudicial to the child
		— (sometimes) over-attachment (between the child and minder), the minder may have the child call her 'Mum' and thus the child may have *two mother images.*

Care by nursery	— guaranteed quality of:
	  education and intellectual stimulus
	  nutrition
	  hygiene
	— presence of other children (better socialisation of the child)
	— opportunity to play outside
	— frequent contact with the mother (special moments in the day are preserved)
	— no risk of over-attachment to one person: 'the nursery is neutral but this sometimes leads to indifference (Soule, 1972)*
	— reasonable cost (means tested)
	— if there is an accident the child is quickly taken to hospital
	— some nurseries are very 'open' to parents.
		— inflexible timetable (the mother cannot fetch her child when she wishes
		— pace of life determined by the group
		— (sometimes) too many children or not enough staff and the children are not properly supervised
		— not enough nurseries–often far from the workplace and this causes problems of transport
		— the child is not taken when he is ill (and an alternative form of care must be sought)
		— risk of contagion which is a feature of all groups
		— lack of affection or preference being shown for some children (child nurses are not always good *substitute mothers!*)
		— a colder, more impersonal environment very different from the family home
		— some nurseries do not include the parents enough in their everyday running and do not inform them about their child's behaviour and so there is a *gap.*

*Soule M 1972 Les modes de garde de l'enfant de O à 3 ans. E.S.F., Paris

THE FULL-TIME NURSERY

Placement in a nursery full-time

Case study

Bernard White is 15 months old. He is a happy, lively child who loves his parents and his brothers and sisters. He is able to walk and can say a few phrases.

His mother has suddenly had to go into hospital following an accident and his father chooses to send him to a nursery for very young children.

The separation itself presents no problems but Bernard soon starts to show signs of distress (crying, restlessness, troubled sleep) and over the next few days refuses all food and sleeps for long periods huddled up. Later these signs of distress gradually disappear to leave the child semi-prostrate. He wears a fixed; expressionless look. He continuously sucks his thumb and rocks in his bed.

And 5 months later when his parents come to collect him from the nursery, they are struck by how docile Bernard is. When he gets home he does not even look at them and seems to have forgotten them entirely. He no longer takes any interest in his toys and when his dog comes over, tail wagging, to greet him he is unable even to talk to him.

Explanation

The child feels that he has been abandoned by his family. He is unable, at this age, to come to terms with a sudden change in care, people, routine surroundings and this gives him a feeling of insecurity.

During the first few days he shows signs of distress which are a kind of cry for help. He is still strong enough to show how much he is suffering by crying and then gradually these signs subside as the child gives in and becomes resigned and detached.

These are signs of serious *'psychological distress'* and are similar to a depression in an adult.

Broadly similar symptoms are also to be found in cases of *'hospitalisation'*.**

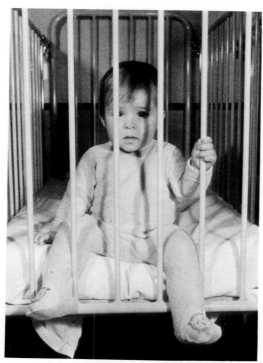

Fig. 3.7

This placement has had an extremely negative effect. It may retard or even cause a regression in the child's psycho-motor development and may store up psychological problems for the future (a child who has suffered will grow into an unbalanced adult).

A placement with a childminder with regular visits from the father and brothers and sisters woud have been greatly preferred.

** Hospitalisation: the term given to all serious disturbances caused by a prolonged stay in hospital. The child's development can no longer progress normally, psycho-motor development is retarded and personality problems occur. The longer the separation lasts the more disturbed the child will be (according to Spitz:' after 5 months the damage is irreparable.').

NURSERY SCHOOL

If there is to be a happy transition from the home to nursery school it is best to send the child once he is 3 years old. The nursery school will help the child to develop his own intelligence and personality.

In effect, according to Professor Bloom[3] 'intelligence measured at the age of 17 has been achieved by 50% between birth and 4 years, 30% between 4 and 8 years and 20% between 8 and 14 years.' This gives some idea of how important pre-school education is to the upbringing of the individual. It is not the role of the nursery school to teach reading and writing but rather to allow the young child to develop in an atmosphere of free activity and to enable him, through play, to gain a greater awareness of his own body and of the outside world.

The nursery school is essential to the child's *socialisation*. It is his first contact with life in a group and, contrary to what people believe when they say 'they do not learn anything at nursery school', what goes on there is vastly more important than actually learning anything.

Origins

Nursery schools came into existence towards the end of the 19th century, were often called kindergartens and were either private or annexed to the primary school. Supervision alone was provided by the teachers. At the beginning of the 20th century enormous advances in child psychology enabled new teaching methods to be devised. Two important names marked this era:

Maria Montessori devised a system of educating the child in accordance with his level of intelligence and her motto was 'help me to do it by myself'.
Decroly thought of focusing the child's attention on a particular topic (for example, exploiting what was happening at the time, looking at the seasons etc.).

It goes without saying that their ideas have had lasting influence on modern teaching methods and that many teachers still derive great benefit from their thoughts and experiences.

Nowadays a great deal of research is being carried out worldwide into developing the best methods for guiding the child's development from the moment he enters nursery school. UNESCO regularly brings together experts from all over the world to discuss this research. Their papers have provided a great deal of valuable material but there is some disagreement and so we should perhaps endorse the experts' view that 'there is still a lot to be learnt about child development and about what is needed to promote healthy intellectual development and lead to a happy, productive life'[4].

The age for starting nursery school

Certain conditions need to be met before the child is ready to go to nursery school. Although nursery schools may accept children from the age of 2 years it is inadvisable to send a child under the age of 3 years. It would, nonetheless, be a mistake to take chronological age as the only rule of thumb. The only really reliable criterion is the maturity of the child.

Generally speaking, the child is ready to go to nursery school when:

— He is 'toilet trained'.
— He can understand and obey 'simple commands'.
— He can 'leave his mother' without a fuss.
— He can walk.
— He has good use of his hands.
— He shows he wants to be with other children.

The individual child's personality should be taken into account. Gesell says that failure to adapt to nursery school is often due to a 'high degree of emotional dependence on the mother or home' and that 'these difficulties are more apparent at the age of 2 years, whereas when the child is 3 years old he will accept nursery school fearlessly'. In fact, at this age, surprisingly enough, there are children who refuse to be collected by their mothers as they want to stay at school for longer.

Gesell also raises the problem of the length of time that the child should spend at nursery school during the day and he believes that 'children become less tired if they only go to nursery school for part of the day and that this is better for their psycho-motor development at this age'. In any event, it is the child's personality which should determine the length of time and also the time of day.

Mrs Rachel Cohen, a doctor in educational science and headmistress of a nursery school, believes that for children between the ages of 2 and 2½ years there should be something different from the nursery 'an environment which has been created for them alone with nursery nurses who can both mother them and be prepared to stimulate the child intellectually and that, in any case, the child should never spend more than a few hours at school each day.'

Unfavourable factors for starting nursery school

It is normal for a child to cry on his first day at school as he feels, to a greater or lesser extent, that he is being separated from his mother and he is anxious and apprehensive about what is new. This generally does not last long and if the teacher knows how to handle the child everything should settle down very quickly and the child will go to school quite happily. There are, however, some unfavourable circumstances which may arise which will affect the child's ability to settle down to nursery school:

— After the birth of a little brother (the child suffers from jealousy and he sees school as rejection).
— After a death in the family.
— After either of his parents has gone in to hospital.
— After a move.
— After having been sent into full-time care.
— After having been bullied by some of his classmates (some submissive children are often picked on by rowdy, aggressive children).
— After problems or clashes with the teacher, etc.

Parents are strongly advised not to send their child to school in the middle of the school year or if he is in poor health.

A child who is not settling down at school will be unwilling to go and may show behavioural upsets of the following nature:

— He may start to suck his thumb again.
— He may wet his bed at night.
— He may have nightmares.
— He may lose his appetite (anorexia nervosa).
— He may cry and throw repeated tantrums.
— He may become agressive { towards his parents / towards his teacher / towards his classmates.

Advice: In such circumstances there is little point in persisting with school as the situation will only get worse and this may retard or even cause a regression in the child's psycho-motor development.

How to prepare for a 'good start' to nursery school

The child should be taught to look on school as a kind of 'promotion' and certainly not as a 'punishment'. The child likes to be thought well of and is always happy to try to behave like a grown up; going to school will provide him with an opportunity to imitate his father by taking his bag with him every morning.

— The mother should prepare for the beginning of term by going out shopping for it (a school bag, pencils, paint . . .).
— The child is curious about everything: parents should play on this imagination by speaking of school as a 'wonderful' place where he will find all the toys he does not have at home and also lots of small friends.
— He should, where possible, be shown the school some days before the start of term so that he has the time to come to terms with the idea of going somewhere new (the playground, toboggans, paintings, etc. should all be pointed out).
— It would be ideal if he already knew one or two of his future classmates (he will feel braver going to school with other people he already knows).

On the first day of term his mother should appear happy and relaxed: she should take her child to school and introduce him to his teacher (who will become a 'second mother' to him and·who may, if all goes well, become a paragon of virtue, of whom the mother, of course, should never be jealous!).

— The mother should avoid lengthy goodbyes as this is always an emotional time for the child.
— In the beginning it is preferable for the child to attend for part of the day only as this will help him to adapt and he will not get too tired.
— In the evening the parents should ask the child about what he has done at school: he needs them to be interested in what he is doing, or rather in him and if he is willing to talk about it his parents will know that all has gone well.

Activities provided for children at nursery school

The type of education that nursery schools provide has always been the pride of state education. Teaching methods are based on 'active participation' and their aim is to encourage the child to progress through play and making things and to enable him to express himself through drawing, painting, song and dance etc. These teaching methods, when used by qualified staff, have proved a very effective means of preparing the child for primary school. The educational syllabus of the nursery school is geared towards making the young child independent in the following areas:

— Physical independence: the child should be able to wash, get dressed and feed himself.
— Moral independence: he should learn to assume responsibility for himself and how to live with other people.
— Intellectual independence: he should learn to observe, analyse and judge his daily activities.

Study of two selected activities: music and movement and painting (see Tables pp. 84–85).

Table 3.4 Music and movement. The child enjoys music, movement and group activities which involve dolls and dressing up. Music and movement is a 'game' which the child greatly enjoys and from which he derives considerable satisfaction

Observation of the children	Objective
The children walk 'in time', 'sing' and 'listen to music'.	Develops activity, a sense of rhythm, good motor co-ordination and gives the impression of happiness. Develops a musical repertoire, the voice and memory.
They stand on one foot.	Develops a sense of balance and dexterity.
They have 'hoops'.	Makes the child aware of his body in relation to other people and objects.
They are going round in a *circle*.	Gives them an idea of the 'organisation of space'; movement in various directions.
They have 'dolls' in their arms.	The idea of symbolism: the doll is associated with the action and helps to recreate 'reality (imitation of mother: sense of responsibility)'.
They dance in front of an *audience*.	They become aware of the 'presence of other people' (the child wants to do his best). Some become more self-confident, others more observant and all develop their *critical faculties*.
They have to do the activity *with other children*.	Concept of the group — helps socialisation through co-operation.
Some children are 'dressed up' and are 'miming' a scene.	Develops the imagination and a sense of make believe which a child of this age needs if he is to come to terms with '*reality*'.
They accept the *rules* of the exercise their teacher has given them.	It teaches them to accept 'rules' and introduces discipline into their socialisation.

Fig. 3.8

Table 3.5 Painting. The child adores 'what he has done himself' and likes being 'creative'. He enjoys using various materials and likes colour and shape and is able to bring what he has made to life thanks to his powers of 'animism'. Painting, in this way, answers his deepest needs.

Observation of the children	Objective
The children hold the brush carefully.	Develops motor co-ordination and manual exterity (and will help the child learn to write).
They follow the '*line*' of a drawing.	As above.
They look for 'colour'.	Develops observation and a sense of colour.
They look at what they are 'creating' with astonishment.	Develops creativity and the child gains in confidence and self-esteem through his work.
They look at their *neighbour's* work.	Develops a critical faculty and spirit of competition (he wants to do 'as well' or 'better').
They all adopt the 'theme' which has been chosen (in this case the farm).	Increases knowledge (here that of the animals on the farm, trees, seasons and the countryside) and this opens the child to the outside world, promotes curiosity, observation, logic and an ability to synthesize.
They sit where the teacher has told them to and they *work in groups*.	Sense of discipline and obedience which leads to the *successful socialisation* of the child.
They have *decorated* their class-room.	Develops a sense of aesthetics and artistic taste.
They bring their painting *to life* and can explain it to an adult.	Develops animism, imagination and articulateness.
They give their painting to their teacher of their mother as a 'present'.	Develops altruism and gives the child the satisfaction of being appreciated for what he has done (self-esteem).
They work 'without making a mess'.	Develops a sense of cleanliness, order and organisation which make the child feel secure.
They *put their things away* once they have finished.	They learn to obey rules and acquire good habits and this aids socialisation.

Fig. 3.9

Creativity

THE CHILD'S DRAWING

The child starts to draw between the ages of 15 and 18 months. In the beginning he only makes '*lines*' unintentionally but he soon starts to produce spirals: this is when he starts to '*scribble*', an activity which he enjoys thoroughly. Once he has produced a scribble he will try to copy it over and over again and this will teach him to control the movement of his hands. With time his scribbles gradually become more realistic drawings through which he is able to reveal himself and which enable him to describe himself and those around him. When he draws he is not concerned with portraying reality: he always has his own, very personal interpretation for his drawings and will be only too happy to explain it.

A child's first drawings are not always made on a sheet of paper. Often they are his spontaneous reactions to a situation: he may trace a pattern in his mashed potato, daub with soup from an upturned bowl or even cover his bed with his excrement. Little attention is paid to these chance events which, nonetheless, have their importance. Parents only start to show an interest in their child's drawing when he has reached a higher level of expression. Towards the age of 1 year there is a period of feverish artistic activity and furniture should be protected from the onslaught of the young artist. Even the walls can provide an enormous canvas for his early attempts. Parents should not be alarmed and

Fig. 3.10

only need ensure that their child is able to express himself without making too great a mess. They should encourage these early attempts. The young child will derive enormous pleasure from giving away the fruits of his labour. He sees drawing as a kind of exchange: he can communicate through it and it provides a bond between him and other people. Thus his spontaneous offer of so valuable a gift should always be accepted with delight. Parents should not be surprised at the child's sudden lack of interest in his work the minute he has given it away: he is only interested in 'doing'. He wonders at his discovery of new sensory and motor possibilities: holding and using a brush or pencil, making bold lines on the paper and even puncturing or tearing it if he presses too hard.

These games, destructive as they may appear, are due to the slow neurological development of the

child: 'it is not only the hands which are engaged in drawing, if the fingers are to become supple the whole body needs to undergo a distribution of muscular tone'.[5]

The child must wait until he is able to stand, walk and control his bowels before he is able to produce scribbles intentionally. He generally reaches this stage from the age of 18 months.

According to Marthe Bernson[6] 'one day the child picks up a pencil and does not put it down. The pencil becomes an extension of his hand and the paper entrances him. The child feels the resistance of the pencil on the paper and enjoys moving the pencil over this limited space'.

The movement of the child's hand leaves a mark on the paper and he wonders at it. He knows that he can repeat this movement and draw something else and that it will be different. It soon becomes possible

Fig. 3.11

to see in his early scribbles the 'beginnings' of a head in the circles and arms in the straight lines and the child will learn to produce a more coherent image when he becomes more aware of his body and of his ability to portray it. The placing of the drawing on the page, its appearance, direction and size are peculiar to each child. Just by glancing through the work produced by a nursery class it is possible to identify the work of each child. Some scribble in the centre of the page, others start drawing round the edge of the page and after zigzagging across the page without lifting the pencil from the paper return to the point at which they started. Psychologists believe that if the pencil is allowed to wander across the page

this reveals the child's need for activity and the fact that some return to where they started reveals a desire to be close to the mother and a search for security.

A great deal of information on the psychology of the child can be obtained through studying his drawings (see p. 92). Drawing, like symbolic games, enables the child to reveal what is going on inside (see p. 96).

Case study

John (2) is happily engaged in drawing a maze of red lines on his little jotter.
While he is producing this never-ending curving line he talks to himself. First we learn that it is a 'Mummy' and then it is a 'baby'. Finally it becomes a 'plane' in the air. Suddenly his drawing takes on a gloomy appearance (he keeps scribbling in the same place). In his amazement he exclaims,

'What a pretty cloud!' When his mother comes over, John is delighted to be able to tell her that this beautiful big circle is a 'horsey' and he is very proud to give it to her.

It is surprising to see the variety of explanations that a child can provide for his drawing and also the a posteriori interpretation which he provides.

The child tries to make his drawing come to life. His interpretation is very subjective and depends on his mood at the time. He only calls the drawing a 'horsey' as that is what he is thinking of at the time. He calls the drawing whatever he wants to appear in it. The drawing is a bridge with his *world of make-believe* and allows him to practise his vocabulary. Until he is 3 years old 'shape' means nothing to him.[7]

It is best to listen to what a child is saying while he is drawing as there is more to be learnt from this than by asking for an explanation of the drawing once it has been completed. The child should never be forced to give an explanation as this might prevent sponataneity and only produce an artificial explanation. Parents should also try not to stifle the child's imagination by teaching him formal rules which will deprive his drawings of all freshness and authenticity. Learning to draw is a slow process as it is dependent on genetic development and cannot be hurried. As in the areas of motor and intellectual development there is no point in trying to force progress: this will take place in its own time and each child will develop at his own rate. Parents

should be content to admire their child's drawings and to encourage him. They should avoid making any unkind comparisons with an older brother or sister who is able to accomplish more. The child sees what he produces as part of himself and if it is scorned he takes it as a personal slight and will tend to underestimate his own ability. Likewise, parents should avoid being excessively flattering. The time will soon come in nursery school when some young 'artists' are highly praised whilst other more personal and authentic drawings, which have been less conditioned by the family, are overlooked.

As regards artistic activity in the creche or nursery school, nowadays some psychologists deplore the contradiction between painting with

the hands and toilet training. Some young children do indeed find it hard to understand why their teacher will accept dirty hands and the daubing of paint when their parents forbid it. I have often observed, in creches, the apprehension of some children at being asked to put their fingers into the paint. They seemed to feel a repulsion at getting their hands dirty but after they had tried it a few times they become totally used to this way of painting.

Obviously a number of teachers are very much in favour of this form of painting as it allows the child to come into direct contact with the material and it allows him to feel completely free to express himself.

The development of graphic expression in the child (Figs 3.12–3.14 — based on Widlocher[8])

15/18 months

18 months/2 years

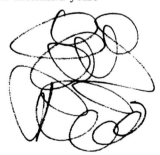

Fig. 3.12 The child makes a lot of horizontal and sloping lines. He is not trying to draw anything but is just enjoying '*making lines*'.

The child is improving his motor control. He wants to imitate adult writing and makes swirls on the paper which are known as '*scribbles*' to which he gives a meaning in accordance with his feelings at the time. The form itself has no intrinsic meaning: this is the age of 'chance realism'[9].

3 years

Fig. 3.13 The child improves his ability to represent objects and he stops scribbling and tries to draw but his apparent mistakes reveal more about the way he sees and perceives the world. It is the age of 'unsuccessful realism'[18].

Whatever his nationality, a child of 3 draws people as 'little tadpole men' with a big head, two eyes and two legs (90% of children draw in this way) as he can now master the 'circle'.

4 years

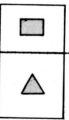

Fig. 3.14 The child can now put a name to what he is drawing, his technique has improved and his drawing gives a better idea of the real world; he does not seek to imitate reality but rather to transpose what he perceives it to be. This is the period of 'intellectual realism'[18] which lasts until he is approximately 9 years old.

One feature of the drawings of children over the age of 4 is their 'transparency': houses reveal their interiors, oceans their fish and there is a whole host of detail which all has meaning to the child.

When drawing a human being the child now adds a trunk, hands, feet (and sometimes hair).

He is able to use the rectangle and the square.

Once the child is 5 years old he starts to use the 'triangle' and extends the shapes he uses. 'Visual realism' does not appear until he is 9 years old when he learns to reproduce reality.

Fig. 3.15

Fig. 3.16

Analysis of the child's drawing

Anyone who wants to find out more about the child should ask him to 'draw' and then to tell the *'story of his drawing'*. This provides insight into his personality.

Modern psychologists increasingly resort to analysis of the child's drawing in order to gain insight into his character and emotional balance. This study covers four main areas: *placing on the page, style, colour* and *content*. 'House, family and tree are the most commonly used symbols.'

Care should be taken not to rush to hasty conclusions: the information in Table 3.6 (p. 92) should be used with caution as the content of a drawing can only be properly analysed by someone who is qualified to do so, i.e. a child psychologist.

CONCLUSION

A child's drawing has a 'spontaneous beauty' which is never sought after for its own sake. The child's intention is to 'suggest', to make something 'come alive' and his drawing, for all its haphazardness, is often guided by the subconscious.

However drawing, like games and language, will soon be modelled on that of the adult and be determined by 'rules' and 'techniques'.

The adult should try to influence the child's drawing as little as possible so that the child is best able to express himself and to develop his own style. A genuine 'education in art' is not a 'training' but rather the 'free discovery' of oneself and others independently of social conditioning.

TOYS

General remarks

'Children who do not have toys are late in coming to grips with reality and never do so to the same extent as other children' according to Edouard Seguin, a forerunner of modern educational methods.

Nevertheless, to this very day there are still people who make a distinction between learning and playing and when an adult talks of a child's game this expression does not fully convey something which not only amuses the child but which also requires an intellectual effort on his part.

It is in the first few years of his life that the child acquires his most lasting impressions of the world which he receives through listening, watching, acting and the environment in which he finds himself is of prime importance and provides what psychologists call 'learning by osmosis'. A child should never remain inactive. He should be stimulated as much as possible and be allowed to experience and discover as much as possible by himself.

The child's first conquest is the world of objects and he makes an effort to understand and control it. The toy is not only a means whereby the child can develop intellectually; it forms a bridge between the complexities of living

Fig. 3.17

Table 3.6

Area studied	Features of the drawing	Interpretation of the drawing
1. *The placing of the drawing on the page*: attention should be paid to the way the child uses the space on the page when drawing.	The child places his drawing at the top or on the right hand side of the page. On the left hand side of the page. At the bottom of the page.	Optimism, humour, idealism, forward-looking, thirst for knowledge. Backward-looking, seeks mother's protection, refusal to grow up. Repression of feeling.
2. *Style*: attention should be paid to the way the child makes lines and handles the pencil.	Heavy, big, straight, strong, vigorous lines. Completes drawing fast Weak, hatched, blurred lines. Curved, sinuous, fine lines. Completes drawing fast. Completes drawing slowly.	Self-confidence, insolence, strong-willed, outgoing, sociable, aggressive. Lack of self-confidence, shyness, instability. Sensitive child. Spontaneous, outward-going child. Methodical, reflective child.
3. *Use and choice of colours*.	Many colours. Few colours: Bright colours. Pale colours. Frequent use of: Black Brown Green Orange Blue Red	A dynamic, open child. An inward-looking child. A sensory child. A rational child. Rebellion. Guilt. Selfishness and egocentricity. A happy relaxed child. Calm, well-balanced. Active, fearless.
4. *The content*: a. *The house* (The house symbolises the child, his surroundings and those who are near to him. It tells about how well he is fitting in at home, about his experiences, his impressions, his personality and his contact with the outside world.)	Small house in the corner of the page. A big house in the centre of the page. Very few windows. Many windows. House without doors or windows. House with doors and windows, a chimney with smoke coming from it and lots of colours. A house surrounded by trees, flowers and birds. A path which leads away from the house. A big fence around the house.	A shy, weak child. A self-confident, energetic child. A secretive, inward-looking child. A confident, outgoing child. Inability to adapt to the outside world. A well-balanced child with a rich inner life. Love for those around him, happiness at being alive. Open to the outside world, eager to grow up. The child does not feel secure.
b. *The family* (This tells us about the atmosphere in the child's home, his relationship with his parents, his conflicts, his desires, his preferences for certain people and even his desire to identify with someone.)	The child's father and mother are drawn to the same scale. The child makes one of the members of the family bigger. The child draws himself small or at the bottom of the page. The child draws himself very big at the centre of the page.	The child considers them as equals. The child considers this person to represent the family, admires him or her or thinks that s/he is the dominant personality. The child feels inferior. The child tends to think too highly of himself.
c. *The tree* (This tells us about the child himself. The *tree* is the *child* as he sees himself, his personality and how he adapts to the world, other people, and his future as he imagines it to be.	Tree with lots of branches. Tree without leaves.★ Tree with lots of leaves. Tall, wide, straight trunk. Thin, curved trunk. Roots buried in the soil.★ No roots A fall of leaves.	Desire for growth (of the mind). Lack of growth. Confident, optimistic, sociable. Active, easy going, strong personality. Sensitive, gentle, refined child who is not very active. Strong instincts, need to be attached. Fits in badly into his family and society. Adapts poorly. Melancholy, nostalgia, instability.

★It is obvious that some of these details should only come under consideration if the child is aware of them!

and the powerlessness of the child.

Life nowadays is becoming increasingly difficult and the child needs objects which enable him to bring reality under control, to affirm his own personality and to learn to socialise. Through toys the child learns to come to grips with the world.

Psychological analyses of play

Play is of such major importance in the life of the child that it has been studied by the two major schools of psychology.

Genetic (or developmental) psychology

This analyses the motor, sensory, intellectual and social development of the child. Its main proponents are Wallon, Gesell and Piaget and is based on an observation of the child's development. It places particular importance on the role of the toy in this development. The toy is considered to be 'an object of experience'.

Psychoanalysis

This is mainly concerned with the emotional behaviour of the child. The toy enables the child to overcome his anxieties, project his fantasies and to communicate with the adult. Its main proponents are Freud, Klein and Winnicott.

In spite of the fact that these two schools hold divergent views on a number of matters, they are agreement that the child can and should use the toy to develop:

— his body
— his intellect
— his affectivity
— his creativity
— his ability to socialise.

The toy helps to develop all these facets of the personality but very few parents are aware of this when they actually choose a toy! And yet the choice of a toy is not an easy task. If a child is given a toy too late he is disappointed by it and if it is given too early he will be discouraged. In order to choose a toy one needs to know the child it is for, his age, his needs, his likes and his behaviour. One also needs to understand the toy and know how it can teach the child and aid his development. This is the only way of being sure that the child receives a balanced range of toys: to only give him toys which are designed to stretch him intellectually is every bit as absurd as to give him only those toys which help him to relate to others.

The role of toys*

Toys for motor development

Toys are an excellent means for developing motor control: this includes overall motor control, i.e. co-ordination and balance (e.g. balls, toys which can be pulled or pushed) and specific motor control, e.g. development of the use of the hands (e.g. posting boxes and toys which have to be fitted together etc.).

Toys for intellectual stimulus

Through playing with a toy the child learns to analyse his movements and make them more effective and less clumsy. He also learns to analyse

* Study on the contribution of toys to the development of the child carried out under the supervision of André Michelet, Centre National d'Information du Jouet (C.N.I.J.), Paris, 1977

objects by taking them apart and putting them together again. He learns how all the different parts come together to form a whole and this constitutes his first step towards learning how to organise objects, a task which will also require reasoning.

There are ranges of toys which enable the child to develop this analytic faculty. These are known as 'educational games' (posting boxes, objects which fit inside each other, jigsaw puzzles and mosaics) but the child needs to be able to apply all that he has learnt to one task. Here is where construction and other similar games are important as they enable the child to analyse space and to reduce the complexities of society to manageable proportions.

The processes of analysis and synthesis which the child applies to these games are not very different to those which he will later use in reasoning and mathematics. They simply provide a material rather than a verbal aid. Since this discovery was made toys have been held in much higher regard as they are seen to develop the child's intelligence in practical tasks as a first step towards abstract reasoning.

Creative toys

The child feels a need to express himself and to let his imagination run free: this helps him to develop a well-balanced personality. Creation does not always necessitate invention. Not all supposedly creative toys require the use of imagination (as do puppets or symbolic games). There are games which teach children how to make things: the child enjoys manipulating them, touching the material he is using and this often leads him to becoming creative.

Symbolic toys

The adult world is not immediately accessible to the young child and he often experiences feelings of conflict.

In order to come to terms with and to eventually grow out of these feelings the child needs to make bonds with objects and to transfer his affections to them. He also needs to imitate actions, re-enact situations and to identify with other people. This helps him to develop self-confidence, understand his role in the family and to come to a better understanding of the adult world which, without the intermediary of play, would remain a mystery to him. The teddy bear and the doll are the most common types of symbolic toy (see special section, p. 96).

Toys which help the child to socialise

In that these toys either prompt or require the child to play with someone else they help the child to understand his relationship with the adult and prepare for socialisation at a later stage. The very young child plays on his own. Later he enjoys being surrounded by other children but they all continue to play on their own. The child needs greater maturity if he is to play with others. He must accept 'rules' and 'self-discipline'. This is the first step towards social organisation. The child is naturally competitive and this is often a part of collective games. This teaches him to evaluate his own capabilities, establish his own personality, to develop self-control,

in short to become a social being.

Note The aforementioned areas are closely interconnected and influence each other.

For example
— games which promote motor development are also often intellectually stimulating.
— creativity has close links with intelligence and emotional development.
— emotional development and symbolism arise from the same roots.
— an emotionally balanced child always socialises well.

Let us take the example of the rattle which plays a role in:
— making the newborn more alert.
— developing the use of the hands.
— stimulating the senses (sight, sound etc.).

Table 3.7 Choice of toys

Needs according to the age of the child	Toys	Benefits
3 to 6 months *The baby likes*: sucking looking hearing new sounds colours and movement.	Plastic teething rings. Little rubber animals. Mobiles hung from the ceiling. A counting frame hung on the cot. Musical boxes. A variety of rattles (the first rattle should be a simple one and preferably red). Crossbars for the cot. *Features* Toys should be rounded, simple in shape, safe, with fast colours (whistles should be removed from toy animals before they are given to the child).	These toys awaken a spirit of discovery, intellectually stimulate the child, teach him about the outside world and promote his ability to observe and adapt to the outside world.
6 months to 1 year The child can control his hands. He can let go of objects at will. He can pass objects from one hand to the other. The child can remain *sitting*. The child has *teeth* (and likes to bite). The child has a *crisis of anxiety* (at around 8 months). The child likes *sound* (music). The child is interested in his *reflection* and his *body*.	A crossbar for the bed. Attachable rattles. Toys for throwing on the ground. Brightly coloured cubes which fit into each other. Balls and bobbins for rolling (in the playpen). Plastic animals for the bath. Plastic animals and tumblers. Teething rings. Brightly coloured rubber keys, rings and triangles. Teddy bear, rag doll. Toys which make a sound. Musical boxes. Mirror games. Games with big balls and cylinders (especially used in nurseries and playgroups).	The manipulation of toys develops the use of the hands, co-ordination and reflexes. Picking up and throwing down objects helps balance and provides a form of gymnastics. The child takes to his mouth toys which have been made for this purpose. Once the child is 8 months old the teddy becomes his friend and confident and has a calming effect as a 'substitute for the child's affections'. Develop hearing. Develop awareness of the self, the sense of touch, the reflexes and courage.

Table 3.7 (contd)

Needs according to the age of the child	Toys	Benefits
1 to 1½ years The child *walks* by himself and is very active. He can *control his hands* and let go of objects with *fine* movements. He likes putting objects *into* others, *removing* them, placing them side by side or on top of one another. He likes *music*.	The child most enjoys running in the garden and going up and down stairs (his hand should be held). A variety of cubes. Cubes, pyramids of rings, tumblers which fit inside each other, picture books with thick pages. Brightly coloured balls to be theaded. Boxes or other objects which can be put inside each other, bucket and spade, plastic moulds and sand, small simple wooden cars. Records for children.	These games develop endurance, vitality and self-confidence in the child and therefore his personality. These stimulate the intellect, teach the concept of volume and a sense of proportion. They develop an awareness of different shapes, the concept of the *container* and the *content*, doing an action over and over again teaches perseverance, will-power and satisfaction with what one has acheived. He develops an ear for music.
2 to 2½ years The child enjoys: throwing pushing pulling dragging balancing sitting astride He likes *touching* substances. He likes *fitting objects together* and *combining* them. He is able to concentrate (and has an inventive mind). He enjoys *scribbling*. He enjoys listening to and telling stories. He enjoys miming. He still enjoys music and children's songs	Coloured balls. Little animals on wheels. Cars and lorries, little plastic articulated trains. Trucks and 'rickshaws'. Rocking horse. Tractors and similar toys which the child can sit on. Earth, water, sand (buckets, rakes, spades, sieves), modelling clay. Letter boxes ⎫ Gears ⎬ educational toys Eggs ⎪ Keys ⎭ Screws and screwdrivers Simple posting boxes Lego Paper and coloured crayons. Water paints and big felt tips. Small children's coloured picture books, post cards. Groups games with songs. Records for children.	The child learns the idea of *moving from one place to another*, speed and he watches out for objects (he quickly solves 'traffic jams'). He acquires a sense of *direction*, an *aim* and a sense of *space*. These games meet his need to come into contact with substances and develop *creativity* (the child grows in self-esteem). These educational toys develop the imagination and require intellectual effort, perseverance, skill, an understanding of volume, shape, relationships and therefore a logical turn of mind. These promote manual dexterity, imagination, creativity and knowledge. They develop language, memory, a sense of rhythm, a love for music, songs and the imagination. When the child plays with others this also helps socialisation.
3 years The child: *identifies* with adults has the faculty of *animism* *Socialisation* (the children start to play in a group but still find it hard to co-operate). *Reflection* *Concentration* *Sense of direction*	Dolls (to play at being mother) Telephones Dressing up outfits – housewife, cowboy, fairy, manicurist etc. Doll's houses Bears, dolls which fit inside each other, dolls with limbs that move. Toboggans Merry-go-rounds Swings Balls Small cars (one child drives and the other pushes). Mosaics, jigsaws and toys with parts to be fitted together. Children's bingo Skittles Toys which are intended to be hit.	All toys at this age involve the child's *imagination*. These games are very important. When the child tries out and imitates what his parents do and think, he is trying to build his own personality. These meet the child's need to expend energy and help him to socialise. These develop logic and intellectual endeavour.

SYMBOLIC TOYS (THE TEDDY BEAR AND THE DOLL)

François Deligny offers those who care for children some very valuable advice drawn from his own personal experience:

— 'if you want to get to know them quickly . . . let them play;
— if you want to teach them about life . . . let them play;
— if you want them to enjoy work . . . let them play;
— if you want to do your job . . . let them play, play . . .'

Play, in fact, makes up the bulk of the child's intellectual and psycho-motor activity. It teaches him about life and it provides him with a refuge from whence he can come to terms with some of its limitations (school, discipline, punishment).

Through 'imitation' the child can act out and experience different roles which he cannot play in real life. As his language grows his games become increasingly complex and while there are some toys which (like fashions) soon go out of date there are others which defy time as the answer to the child's deepest needs: these are symbolic toys of which the two most common are the teddy bear and the doll. These are the real toys, the ones the child loves best.

The teddy bear

Case study
John (5) has been sent to hospital for a small, emergency operation. He thought that his family had abandoned him and in his distress refused to eat. His mother, in the panic of taking him to hospital, had forgotten his little friend 'Teddy'! When she brought it a few days later John immediately started to smile. He had to have 'horrible injections' every day and now he decided he would cure his bear by subjecting him to the same fate. Teddy cried a little at the beginning but on John's advice decided it was better not to make a fuss as he would get a 'sweetie as a reward'.

When he returned home John was delighted with his new profession and even asked his parents for a nurse's outfit.

What neither the nursing staff or his parents were able to do was accomplished by 'Teddy'. Through the imitation of adults the child manages to overcome difficulties in life and makes an important step forward. The toy provides an essential bridge to adulthood. The almost sacred role of the teddy has long been recognised and in the eyes of the child this object takes on almost magical powers. According to Winniciott[10] 'its role is to "effect" a link between what is going on in the child's mind and the outside world of people and things.' The newborn makes no distinction between the outside world and himself, his mother satisfies his every need and gives him infinite pleasure. The bear comes into the child's life at the time when he realises that his mother is not a part of himself and when he perceives his mother as a separate entity (generally around the age of 7–8 months). He also discovers that his bottle does not always come on time and that his mother does not always appear the instant he calls for her. He thus starts to differentiate between himself and the outside world.

The softness and warmth of his bear remind him of 'contact' with his

Fig. 3.18

mother. Touch is supremely important as it comforts the child and provides security and well-being.

Spitz[11] was the first to experiment with dolls made out of iron and those which were soft. He offered both to newborns and all, without exception, turned towards the more human feel of the soft toy.

The child will turn his teddy into a kind of a mascot. He takes all his woes to it, is comforted by it and looks to it for compensation. Is the child aware that this is pure illusion? This really depends on the age of the child and on how great is his need. Some adults also turn to certain objects for compensation and these objects, normal as they may seem, are a form of 'substitute'. So the teddy, the child's faithful companion in times of distress, is a subject eminently worthy of all our attention.

The doll

Case study

Virginia (3) often plays with her doll 'Maggie'. She feeds her, changes her nappies, sings her a lullaby and then wakes her up again to take her to a circus, out shopping or to the swimming pool (to learn to swim). She has been talking to her for a long time now about a wonderful plan she has, 'We're going, just the two of us, on a long trip. We're going very far away, by sea, in a big white ship.' But Maggie starts to cry. 'You must be very good or you won't be able to come with me,' scolds Virginia. Maggie does not stop crying and her little mother comes and leans over her cot and says gently, 'I'm sorry Maggie, I didn't realise, you didn't want me to close the door, you're scared of the dark. I'm going to take you to bed with me tonight and you'll be all right.'

Listening to Virginia spend hours talking happily to her doll, it is easy to see how she lives in a world of her own where she re-enacts scenes she has experienced and peoples them with those who are near to her.

When she scolds the doll and threatens to punish it she is learning to accept this situation in her own life. When she gives her doll the bottle, tells it stories and talks about her holiday plans she is identifying with her parents and making the adult world her own.

Through play, the roles are reversed: the doll is Virginia and Virginia is the adult (mother, father or teacher according to her need at the time).

The child attributes the doll with all the feelings she herself experiences: 'If the doll drops her eyelids she is sad', 'If she falls she is ill'. These symbolic games help us to understand what is going on in the child's world, what he likes or does not like, what hurts him and what fascinates him (here the boat trip, the closed door and the fear of the dark are all charged with inner meaning).

The symbolic game both reassures and compensates. The child is able to throw off fear and anxiety and become well-adjusted.

Why does everyone remember the mysterious love they felt for their dolls? No doubt it is because

Fig. 3.19

they are fashioned in our own image. Children quickly realise that the doll is not real although it remains so for their inner self. At the age of 1 year the child clasps it to his chest, may throw it to the floor or even hit it. Once he is 2 years old he handles it with all his mother's gestures and when he is 3 years old he starts to identify with it as the doll has become his double. It is only when the little girl is 7 or 8 years old that she will start to project her vanity on to the doll by finding it elaborate clothes to wear. Furthermore, in talking to the doll the child does not only develop his use of language but also his whole personality.

Advice on the choice of doll in relation to the age of the child

— Soft, stuffed, baby dolls, for example a 'rag doll' which is soft to the touch and easy to handle are ideal for children between the ages of 1 and 1½ years.
— Towards the age of 2–3 years the doll can be more realistic: the child likes to be able to see the eyes and mouth and to play with the doll's hair. It should however be a simple sturdy toy. At this age it is extremely inadvisable to buy an expensive doll; the child may admire it but will not dare to touch it. He will quickly abandon it for his beloved old dolls which he cannot spoil.

If the child is to have a doll which he likes he must be able to choose it for himself. He should be taken to a toy department and if he falls in love with a particular doll then that is the one for him, even if his parent does not like it as the relationship between a child and his doll is one of true love.

THE CHILD AND MAKE-BELIEVE

Once the child is 2 years old he enters a world of make-believe. The young child needs to believe in make-believe if he is to become well-adjusted, develop his personality, imagination and knowledge of the world and to learn to socialise.

The child also, with the help of his parents, needs to be able to leave this world behind him and progress towards maturity. Each child does this in his own time and parents should make an effort to understand and respect this.

Make-believe reassures the child

as it answers a deep-seated need for security. The child seeks refuge in this imaginary world which is free from adult rules. It cushions him from reality and when he does come up against difficulties he will be better able to cope.

Natalie does not like leaving her parents in the evening to go to bed but when she has her dog with her they have a little talk before going to sleep and everything is fine.

Peter refuses to eat his soup; when his mother gives a spoonful to his teddy who immediately cries 'more' he wants to race his teddy and be finished first.

Make-believe increases the child's knowledge of the real world

When John (3) plays with his cubes he is not simply content to make a row of them. He decides that they are going to be a 'little train' on its way into the country. Suddenly he puts one cube on top of another and decides that that is the family off on a trip in the train. He also makes a train noise, 'Chuff, chuff'.

I have spent long periods in nurseries observing young assistant child nurses using similar games to help the children develop their imagination, knowledge and use of language. The nurse might ask:

'And where are we going on the train?'
'On a picnic,' the children reply.
'And what are we ging to take?'
'Bread and cakes,' the children answer.
'What if we took some wood? Or some leaves?'
'We could take chestnut leaves, sycamore leaves and what about some smells?' the little girls suggest.
'Take a deep breath and just smell the flowers, the dead leaves, the tree.' (Sniff, sniff!)

During this totally imaginary picnic I saw how much the children enjoyed 'miming' the ritual of the meal. They would not have enjoyed a real picnic nearly so much. The child likes to imitate the world of the adult as this enables him to bring it under his control.

Make-believe aids socialisation

If a child has a bad experience he tries to come to terms with it by setting it in a different context.

Through play, the child feels indispensable, he is no longer a small, impotent being in a world not built to his scale. He likes to frighten himself so that he can overcome the difficulty. Difficulties provide him with the opportunity experiencing fear, becoming used to it and overcoming it.

John, by nature a very timid child, is particularly fond of dressing up in his cowboy outfit and holding at bay a whole tribe of Indians who dare not emerge from behind the dresser.

The child draws strength from the world of make-believe and this enables him to accept the limitations

Fig. 3.20

imposed by living with others. When the little girl is playing with her doll she might call her doll anything from 'a good little girl' to 'a horrible little girl with filthy hands' to 'a bad pupil.' Depending on her needs at the time she will become her mother, her big sister or her teacher and she is able to create comforting self-images. This kind of play makes her stronger and more independent, more able to accept adults and allows her to plan out how she is going to react when similar situations arise in the future.

The child must be able to leave the world of make-believe

The day will come when the child must leave his childhood behind and adapt to the adult world: he must therefore grow out of the world of make-believe. If he does not make the break he will become cut off from the outside world and be unable to grow psychologically and morally.

Once he is 4 years old he is able to take the first step: the child no longer constructs a world of make-believe for himself alone and enjoys playing with others at doctors and nurses and mummies and daddies.
He gradually adapts to society. Some children do, however, experience some difficulty in making the transition between make-believe and reality.

Sylvia (10) does not like playing with other children of her own age and is only happy when she is on her own in her bedroom with her doll. She spends hours telling her doll about all the little upsets she has had during the day.

It is obvious that more should be done to help children like these and to encourage them to accept the real world even if they do find it disappointing.

Parents are partly to blame for some obsessive anxieties which can impede their child's progress.

Charles (8) is frightened that if he does not eat up his soup a bogeyman will come and carry him off down to his cave.

Parents should always beware of feeding the child's imagination with such terrifying and false stories.

Parents should attempt to prepare the child for the real world while trying to preserve his enthusiasm, spontaneity and naturalness without which he will lack creativity and charm. This is a difficult task. Each child progresses at his own rate and those who cling the longest to their world of make-believe should not be made fun of. Parents should gently try to make the child aware of certain facts of life and when he is a little older should try and channel his imagination not towards television or comic book heroes but rather towards the great men and women of science, history and religion. There is no dearth of impressive people whose will-power and perseverance have ensured their success. Young and old are able to enthuse together. What obviously is important is that parents should not talk to a child of 12 years in the same terms as they would use to a child of nursery school age.

Parents should also learn to respect their child's secrets: many parents are lacking in tact and openly make fun of a story they have overheard by chance or a note that they have found. They destroy the fantasy which every individual needs and will cause their child to turn in on himself even more. Parents should rather, even if they find a situation absurd, be prepared to enter the game so that they can come to a better understanding of their child and be able to help him overcome his problem. Parents need to be able to laugh with their children. It should not be forgotten that what makes an individual's personality is that part of his childhood that he has been able to retain.

The major stages in a child's upbringing

TOILET TRAINING

In the life of a child there are some achievements which are more important than others and which remain in the child's memory for a long time. Such is the case with toilet training. Just like the first step, the first tooth or the first smile, toilet training marks a milestone in the child's life. Toilet training presents two major advantages: it simplifies the mother's life considerably (no more nappies) and it allows the child to become more independent (he can now go to nursery school).

Nevertheless, toilet training, as an acquisition, does depend to a greater extent than others on the mother. The child has to be taught to become toilet trained. It also depends on the physiological development of the child and as such cannot be hastened.

Three prerequisites for toilet training

A child cannot be toilet trained until his nervous system has matured to the extent that he can control his bladder and bowels. Thus there is a 'physiological' prerequisite. In the newborn the bladder empties automatically as soon as it is full. In the toilet trained child the process is different. When the bladder (or the bowel) is full the child feels it and becomes aware of his need and this is when he .decides (if he has the opportunity) whether to open or close his sphincter*. He can even

hold back while waiting for his pot. Thus the child needs to be able to understand what is expected of him and he must be capable of giving a warning (even if it comes too late!) and he therefore needs to be able to communicate. This is an 'intellectual prerequisite'.

Furthermore, once the child has understood what is expected of him, he must want to respond in order to please others. This is an 'emotional prerequisite'. It is obvious that these three prerequisites are very closely interconnected and complement each other: if any one was lacking the child would be unable to be toilet trained.

Toilet training is a very lengthy, gradual process which sometimes suffers setbacks due to the child's state of mind at the time as 'it is his emotional make-up which determines progress'[12]. The birth of a little brother may, for example, upset toilet training. The child is jealous and upset. He soils himself in a bid for attention.

The child first learns to control his bowels and then his bladder (human beings of all ages have greater difficulty in controlling their bladder than their bowels). Likewise the child may learn to remain clean during the day long before he also remains clean at night. This is because the young child sleeps too deeply to become aware of his need. With time his sleep will change and he will learn to wake up and call his

* sphincter: a circular muscle, contraction of which serves to close an orifice (anal sphincter for the bowel and vesical sphincter for the bladder).

mother or to get up and go to the pot by himself if he needs to during the night.

The child becomes toilet trained between the 15th and 30th month.

At 36 months (3 years) the child should be clean both day and night. However bedwetting should not be a ground for concern before the child is 4 years old. In most cases this is due to psychological problems which are upsetting the child.

Development of toilet training — the various stages can be seen in Table 3.8.

Table 3.8 The stages of toilet training

	Control of bowel	Control of bladder
12 months	Many mothers already start to toilet train their children from this age onwards. It should be remembered, however, that changes in the nervous system in preparation for the child learning to stand upright and walk slow down, to a considerable extent, his ability to control his bladder and bowel. Therefore there is little point in putting pressure on the child. At this age there are very few instances of successful toilet training.	The child may be dry after his afternoon nap but if he is put on his pot he struggles to get away. Parents should not insist that he stays.
15 months	The child is extremely interested in his new capacity to *retain* or *expel* faecal matter. He becomes aware of discomfort, of a need and realises that he can do something about it. He experiences a feeling of well-being and physical *pleasure* in moving his bowels but soon realises that his little game of deciding whether or not to move his bowels may run counter to his mother's wishes. The child moves his bowels twice a day: generally when he wakes in the morning and after his afternoon nap. The baby's habits should be studied and he should be put on his pot when he is most likely to want to go. Nonetheless, while the child is perfectly capable of refusing to pass a motion when sitting on his pot he has not the same bowel control when standing up and therefore might suddenly move his bowels when his mother stands him up or puts on a clean nappy. The child is not yet in sufficient control of his anal sphincter to be able to contract and relax it at will. The child can show his mother that he has dirtied himself by showing her his pants or by making a fuss. He wriggles and might even try and take his troublesome nappy off himself. At this age the child may often move his bowels when he is in bed or in his playpen. He goes red in the face and if there is no-one on hand he is likely to start playing with his faecal matter (*daubing* is a favourite pastime at this age). The child should have his nappy firmly done up so that his mother should never have occasion to say that he is dirty or to scold him (as this attitude can be extremely prejudicial to successful toilet training) (see advice, p. 105).	The child may go for 2–3 hours before emptying his bladder. He may refuse to sit on the pot if his mother does not choose the right moment. If the mother knows how to handle him and chooses the right moment he may sit quietly on the pot for a short while but does not always do what is required of him. Very often he chooses the very moment that his mother lifts him of the pot or changes his nappy to do 'a wee wee and a pooh' at the same time. He is not being wilful or unco-operative but rather clumsy much as can be observed in his lack of dexterity in dropping things. The child is not yet capable of relaxing his muscles gently and therefore it is a sudden movement. Control depends on his nervous system. The child can point to, with a knowing look, a little puddle on the living room floor and even say 'wee wee'. In his eyes nothing is dirty and he will enjoy himself touching and splashing his urine. This is a common action in a child of this age and reveals his curiosity (for this as for everything else) and his desire to find out more about his urine (after all it comes from him and is very intriguing). Parents are strongly advised not to leave their child on the pot for too long and not to scold him if he fails to pass water as he will stop letting them know when he needs to go (see advice, p. 105).
18 months	The child is not as regular as he was at 15 months. He is equally likely to sit on his pot after his nap, after meals, mid-morning or mid-afternoon. (Some children do however go regularly after meals and they are much easier to toilet train.) Different children participate in their toilet training in different ways. Some, who have a facility with language,	The child's use of language improves and he can more easily make himself understood and say when he has dirtied himself or wet his nappy. He finds it easier to remain on his pot if he is sitting comfortably. He has no trouble in understanding his mother's questions, 'Do you want to wee wee?' 'Do you want your pot?' and often says no; when he

Table 3.8 (contd)

	Control of bowel	Control of bladder
18 months	can express their need by a simple word, 'Wee wee, biggie, pooh etc' but often only say the word after the action has taken place. It is already something that the child can link word and action. Others are happy just to pull at their pants. Some do not say or do anything and it is only their sudden immobility (or red face) which alerts the parent who must hurry for a pot!.	does want to go it will be sudden and parents have to act quickly! Most children of this age continue to wet themselves without saying anything and are impatient and may even struggle if their parents want to sit them on the pot too frequently or at the wrong moment.
21 months	At this age, for some children who were previously making good progress, there is a short period of regression.[1] The child dirties himself and cries. His muscles relax in a sudden, explosive fashion. The child expends so much effort that he often cries out (especially when passing a motion). He is aware of what is expected of him but he is unable to control himself and may wet or dirty himself 'before he was expecting it'. At this age he is often scolded as his parents think that he has 'done it on purpose'. This is a dangerous attitude as the child would like to be clean but cannot yet control his bladder or bowel. If the child is used to being scolded he will blame it on someone else (and this is his first lie born out of fear). This should be avoided. Sometimes the child feels so guilty that he rushes into his mother's arms for forgiveness before she has had the chance to scold him. It is at this age that some parents, who are in a hurry to have their child trained, wake him up during the night to avoid him wetting himself. This does not always meet with success and can seriously affect the child's ability to sleep.	
2 years 2½ years	The child can control his bowel better. He may *remain clean during the day*. He can make himself understood and give advance *warning* (baby pooh, John biggie). He can go to the toilet or the pot by himself and try to take down his trousers (he does not always manage to do so). He can tell his mother that he wants to be left alone on the pot as he likes to be in charge. This illusion should not be shattered as it will help him to become successfully toilet trained.	The child is able to control his bladder for longer periods, up to 2 hours at a stretch. The child finds it difficult to control his bladder and may still have problems during the day. Some children are dry one week and then start to wet themselves the next; others are dry every other day. Others, despite their good intentions, always reach the pot too late. His pants are already wet and the child is upset when he discovers his 'little accident' and often starts to cry. Girls are more likely to become dry quicker than boys but it is not really known why this should be.
	The child still dirties himself at night.	
3 years	The child passes between one and two motions a day (often after meals or first thing in the morning – this depends on the child). He might also miss a whole day. The child goes to the toilet or pot by himself, does not like being disturbed and often closes the door. He *congratulates* himself on what he has done ('Good boy John') and often talks to his faecal matter ('Not nice! Yuck!') always using phrases he has heard from his parents. Despite his desire to be independent, the child still needs his parents to wipe him once he has finished.	The child is dry *during the day* and can control his bladder much better. He can now go for 3 hours before passing water and tells his mother beforehand. He can now express himself well and has no difficulty in making himself understood. If he needs to go during the night he can get up go to the toilet by himself or call for his mother to get up. Accidents do not happen very often but they can occasionally occur until the child is 3½ years old.
3½ years	*Child is clean day and night*	

*This table of the various stages of toilet training is based on the works of Arnold Gesell. It should only be used as a guide for, as Gesell said himself, 'Progress never goes in a straight line, there will be ups and downs, irregularities and differences in progress from one child to another.'

[1]According to Gesell; 'This regression leads us to believe that there is a *transition stage* at this age, when new controls of the nervous system start to come into play.'

The child's experiences

Curiosity

The young child finds faeces a peculiar object and treats them with an often anxious curiosity. On the one hand, because this object was once part of himself he feels that his body is being 'broken up'[13] and that something has left him. On the other hand, this object belongs to him, is a part of him and as such

Fig. 3.21

can only be good.

The child finds the whole situation extremely confusing. He does not understand why one minute his mother wants him to sit on the pot and congratulates him for what he has done and the next minute calls it dirty, wants to get rid of it as quickly as possible, seems almost disgusted by it and will not let him touch it (as if it were something dangerous!).

Anal pleasure

When a child produces faeces he feels a type of pleasure known as 'anal gratification'. 'The content of the intestine acts as a stimulant'.[13] 'Erogenous activity in this zone is originally much more important than might be imagined considering the extent to which it has been repressed'.[14]

The mouth is the erogenous zone in the newborn and this is the *oral phase*. Once the child is 15 months old the erogenous zone moves to both sphincters and this constitutes the *sado-anal phase*. This somewhat surprising term implies that when the child produces faeces he feels that he is expelling something bad, an irritant and he feels that he is destroying it. This is what has led psychoanalysts to draw a parallel between this (sadistic) expulsion and nascent aggression in the child.

The desire to possess and to give

The child will then start to seek gratification in retaining and not in expelling. The mother asks the child to wait and not to soil his pants. The child only does this in order to gratify his mother. The child also wants to be able to control himself. If he knows that this pleases his mother and if he is encouraged he will be even more delighted. He will produce faeces as a gift for his mother. The child sees it in terms of a gift and gives it to her as a sign of his love and obedience. If he refuses, it is a sign of obstinacy. 'Retention of faecal matter is often at the root of chronic constipation in certain neurotics'.[13]

Case studies

Gary has just done his 'business' on the pot and gets up and casts a curious eye over it. He puts his finger in the precious matter to test its consistency and calls his mother. 'Mummy, nice pooh!' His mother does not arrive immediately and Gary decides to take the pot through into the kitchen to let her admire what he has done. Unfortunately he drops some on the way but he is very proud of himself. Mum congratulates him and suggests that they both go and empty it down the toilet. Gary holds the pot firmly in both hands and carries it through and tips it gaily into the toilet. He is very proud of his exploit and turns his cheek up to his mother for a kiss.

Virginia does not want to stay on her pot. She grumbles the minute her mother tells her to sit on her pot. Her mother tries to sit her on it and Virginia stiffens, wriggles and resists. Her mother scolds her and Virginia runs away into the flat. Her mother catches her, smacks her bottom and sits her back on the pot. Virginia stays on the pot but refuses to co-operate. Instead she pushes herself, on her pot, around the room. From time to time she shows her mother the empty pot with a sly look. Her mother sits her back down and looks pleadingly at her. After 20 minutes still nothing has happened. Her mother picks her up briskly, tells her that she is a naughty girl and that she will never grow big and strong like Christine (her elder sister) and warns her that her father will scold her when he comes home. Virginia unhappily goes into the next room to comfort herself with her toys. A moment later she starts crying and her mother looks in to see that she is dirty!

For toilet training to be successful

Parents and all those who work with children should remember that for all kinds of training, and in particular for toilet training, caution is of the essence as here the child is being required to control a bodily function. This training can only be of value if it is achieved by the child himself. The adult is only there to help.

Advice

Regularity should be achieved gradually. A regular routine allows the body to form habits but this routine should be based on a study

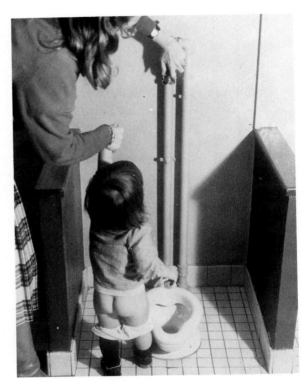

Fig. 3.22

of the child's natural habits. Once the child is 15 months old nappies should be replaced by pants so that the child becomes more aware of his bodily functions. The child should never remain on the pot for more than 5 minutes and he should feel comfortable on it. If he prefers to sit on the family toilet he should be allowed to do so. It is best to seek the child's collaboration and to look for initiatives on his part as this is the most likely way to obtain successful results and earlier independence as well as a well-balanced personality.

Place importance on toilet training. Parents should emphasise the social importance of toilet training: once a child is toilet trained he can 'go to nursery school' and 'do it like Mummy and Daddy'. The child is very sensitive to any argument which stresses the importance of toilet training. When he is successful he must receive praise so that he knows he is doing the right thing. Even if he has dirtied his pants by mistake parents should admire what he has done. Parents should also know how to do things with him. A child of this age is only too happy to imitate his mother. She should teach him to flush the toilet after him (like her). Parents should avoid toy pots (for example, those in the shape of a duck!) or seats that can be turned into pots as the child is then unable to identify the real function of the pot and this detracts from its importance. Parents should remember that the child wants to become toilet trained to become like a grown up.

To be avoided

The use of force. Training children is not like training animals. A child should never be forced to sit on the pot and no pressure should be exerted on what he does and when he does it. Most importantly, he should never be scolded if he does not produce an immediate result. This only produces subservience and makes the child totally dependent on the adult thus producing anxiety which has a bad psychological effect on the child and may mark him for life. Toilet training should be based on love and affection. If the child feels that his mother is using toilet training as a weapon against him, he may refuse to be trained and he may dirty himself as a weapon against her.

Making fun of the child and making comparisons. If the child is told that he is 'dirty' and is unfavourably compared with other brothers and sisters, he will feel hurt, guilty and humiliated especially if he does not find these accusations justified. Feelings of impotence and weakness along with the fear of dirtying himself will produce a worried, timid, frightened child who is frightened to make an effort or of tackling anything new.

Waking the child at night. Some parents who want to train their child as quickly as possible may waken him twice or three times during the night. The child will have difficulty sleeping, become nervous and often resist. Parents should avoid reducing their child's consumption of water in the evening as his body generally needs it.

Enemas. The child sees these as an aggression against his person and feels that he is being taken advantage of.

Conclusion

Toilet training is closely linked to the child's general upbringing. Its aim is to enable the child to control his bodily functions and thus to become more independent and to learn to socialise. Many people strongly believe that toilet training requires a sustained effort on the part of the parents. Toilet training should not be seen as a kind of conditioning. 'In most cases it is the mother who is being conditioned and not the child' according to Professor Lelong. On the contrary, the child must learn to act on his own and the role of the parent is to choose the most opportune moments and methods of helping the child progress towards becoming fully toilet trained. A great deal of disappointment can be traced back to a lack of understanding of this fundamental notion.

INFANT SEXUALITY

Freud, the founding father of psychoanalysis, gave a stunning account of how the adult personality stems from childhood experience, experience which, as a tiny child, he has buried in his subconscious. When, on his death bed, he was asked what his greatest discovery had been, he jested, 'I discovered that children had a sex!'

What he intended was to remind the public that, during his entire lifetime, his work had been subjected to perpetual attack by its opponents and that, like many great thinkers, he had great difficulty at the time in convincing people of certain truths which are nowadays universally accepted.

The gratifications of the newborn
(the oral and anal stages)

The child is a sexual being and this starts at birth.

At this age it is probably more apt to use the term 'gratification' rather than 'sexuality'.

The newborn experiences a physical feeling of pleasure when he sucks his mother's breast. He receives oral pleasure through sucking: there is the warm feeling of milk entering his mouth and the feeling of relief from the painful tension of hunger which prompted him to suck in the first place. One need only look at the satisfied look on the baby's face to see this!

This feeling of pleasure closely linked to the mouth is what Freud called the 'oral stage'.

The pleasure the child derives from breast feeding and the mother's presence create a need for contact.

This pleasure, which is an

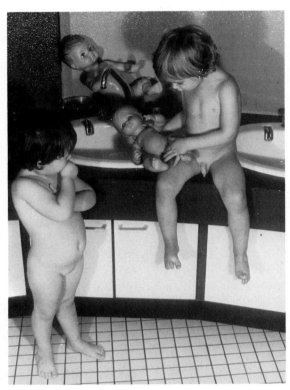

Fig. 3.23

elementary form of love, is focused on the mother and provides an initial touch-stone for the child's progress: it arouses his interest in something outside himself, something which he can see, touch and know to be present and this makes him happy.

By sucking his thumb the baby rediscovers the same oral pleasure as he derives from breast feeding.

This oral stage is followed by what Freud has called the 'anal stage'. The child discovers pleasure in passing, or not passing a motion.

What is the nature of this 'anal gratification'? According to Freud,

the child feels pleasurable sensations locally as the motion moves down the intestine and is finally passed. It is therefore a kind of physical pleasure.

As in the oral stage, this pleasure is connected with the mother.

The child feels that he has done well and has lived up to her expectations.

It is therefore a pleasure directed at his mother and it is also motivated by psychological factors (see p. 103).

The genital stage

Already at a very early age the child

becomes aware of the differences between the sexes but he does not give it the same importance as the adult: initially, he perceives a difference in roles, tasks carried out within the family, differences in the way his parents dress.

By the age of 2–3 years the child starts to look a little further and, with nudity being more fashionable nowadays, has many opportunities in the family home to observe for himself the differences between the sexes of his father and mother and his brothers and sisters and himself.

He is very concerned by this 'difference' and there are people who maintain that it can shock the child but here everything depends on the attitude of the parents towards a situation which, whether one likes it or not, is to a certain extent taboo.

The child's discovery of the difference between sexual organs by no way means that he has discovered sexuality (although Freudian theories maintain the reverse).

Initially the child merely observes the difference between sexual organs and this is particularly the case during toilet training when his eyes are often drawn to how people go to the toilet.

By the very number of questions he asks, the child reveals his fascination for this part of the body. He sets off to discover his own body and that of other people. It is perfectly natural for him to discover his own sexual organs.

He does not restrict his discoveries to what the eye can see, he uses his hands to be more precise.

Let us now look at some photographs of children (p. 107) and study our own reactions to the children's attitudes.

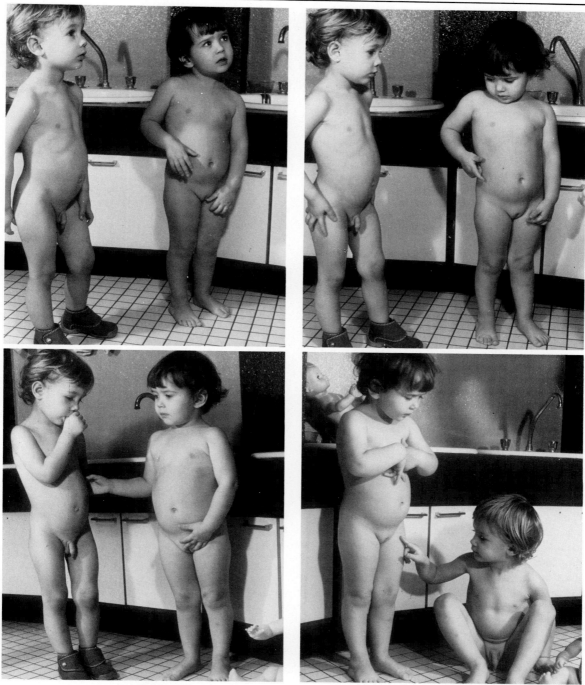

Fig. 3.24 A little boy and girl are enjoying playing together naked. They display their genital organs in total innocence. They see nothing wrong in touching them or taking a close look at them except if their mother comes in and says something which spoils it all. 'Shame only arises out of a knowledge of evil. If these children know no evil, how then are they to feel shame? To teach them shame merely teaches them that there are things to be ashamed of and fills them with a secret desire to discover these things' (Jean-Jacques Rousseau in *Emile*).

WHAT ARE THE INNOCENT STAGES OF THIS DISCOVERY?

THE CHILDREN'S BEHAVIOUR

They observe their genital organs with interest, displaying a healthy interest.

They touch their genital organs to find out about them just as they did with their hands, feet and objects.

They are astonished by their new discovery as can be seen from their faces.

They ask questions on their own level, very simple, naive questions. The little girl sees that the boy has something she does not have (this is what leads to envy) and the little boy sees that the girl lacks something (this leads to worry).

Let us quote a sample of what the children might say:

The little boy might look at the girl and say 'Baby's hurt'.

'I want a tap too,' the little girl might say when she sees that the boy has something she does not. Sometimes the child calls it by words such as 'a widdle' which refer to its function.

They immediately tell their mother about their discovery and this shows the trust they have in their mother.

Children ask their parents lots of questions if they see them naked in the bathroom and even want to 'touch' to find out better. This is normal, healthy curiosity. Young Hans, in Freud's famous book said, 'Mum, have you a willy?'*

3-year-old children often make comparisons of sexual organs when they are in the presence of animals.

On seeing a cow, little Hans said to his parents: Why is milk coming out of its willy?* And when he sees a locomotive ejecting water he said: Where is its willy? Children of the ages of 5 and 6 years often play at mothers and fathers and doctors. This is often a pretext for seeing each other naked and touching each other and sometimes at this age they hide to do this. They have already understood the taboos which surround this whole area. All children go through this stage and there is no cause for concern. However parents should be careful that an older child does not exploit the games of these children.

* Psychoanalysis of little Hans published in *5 psychanalyses de Freud* based on the notes of a father on the questions asked by his 4-year-old son.
† Permanent hostility towards the parent of the same sex may cause the child to become subconsciously extremely attached to the parent of the opposite sex. A boy, for example, who is unable to come to terms with his own sex and rejects virility may be drawn towards

THE PARENTS' BEHAVIOUR

Negative attitudes

The parents are ill-at-ease when their children ask them questions or show an interest in sexual matters.

They are very hard on the child thinking that he is depraved or at the very least losing his innocence.

They avoid questions.

They pull the children away from each other roughly.

They scold or smack their children and this can lead to the child being seriously disturbed.† They threaten the child in a variety of ways. Let us take the example of little Hans who was caught with his hand on his penis.

'If you do that again, the doctor will come and cut off your willy'. (This kind of threat gives rise to anxiety, fear, guilt and a variety of complexes in the child.)

They refuse to give explanations, because they project their own embarrassment on to the child and wrongly believe that the child's view of sexuality is the same as their own.

Positive attitudes

They answer easily and naturally. They are not shocked by the child's questions.

They are delighted with their child's curiosity which they see to be perfectly normal and valid.

They answer each question clearly which reassures the child. For example:

When talking to a little girl they might say, 'You don't have a little tap but you do have little breasts which one day you can use to feed your baby.'

And when talking to a boy they might say, 'You have a little tap like your father. Your sister is like your mother. It's quite normal.'

They do not scold the child. They do not impose on him unnecessary rules of modesty. They try not to forbid him to do too many things but if he seems too interested in his genital organs they try to channel his interest elsewhere.

They explain sex to the child in simple terms with the aid of perhaps photographs of animals. They try not to say too much but reply to the child's questions in terms which he can understand.

homosexuality (which is, according to Freud, 'a transformation of the self into the image of the parent of the opposite sex' which explains effeminacy and an attraction towards the same sex).

RESULTS

The attitude of the parents towards sexuality determines the reactions of the child to a large extent

They teach the child that sexuality is shameful, dirty, taboo. They feed his imagination with worrying fears.

They effectively make him all the keener to find out what he perceives as being shrouded in mystery.

They reassure the child and make him feel secure and this means that he has and will have a balanced view of sexuality. They channel the child's interest elsewhere.

They inspire trust between parent and child.

The oedipal stage

Case study

Virginia has displayed a particular interest in her father over the past 2 months. When he comes home she rushes over to tell him about what she has done during the day. She wants him to play with her, put her to bed and kiss her goodnight. At the weekend when they go to the country, she enjoys racing across the fields with her father but when her father and mother walk together arm in arm she pushes in between them to separate them. She takes her father's hand and pushes her mother away!

Once a child is 3 years old, he not only experiences physical sensations but he also has feelings and he starts to love his father and mother in the true sense of the word although these feelings are somewhat ambivalent. A sexual element is clearly present in the relationship between the child and the adult. His libido draws him towards the parent of the opposite sex and leads him to reject the parent of the same sex.

Freud analysed this situation in depth and in memory of the Greek hero who was fated to marry his mother and kill his father, he called it the *Oedipus complex*.[16] In short, the small boy is in love with his mother and the girl is in love with her father. A child of this age is nonetheless aware of the bonds between his father and mother: the small boy realises that his love for his mother must be shared with his father and the same is true for the girl and her mother.

The child finds it hard to accept that someone else should take his place so often. He wonders why his parents shut themselves away in

Fig. 3.25

their bedroom in the evening and walk about arm in arm. He thought he was the loved one and now he wonders why he is left out so often.

The parent of the same sex becomes a rival to whom the child shows feelings of hatred or jealousy. Psychologists have collated a great number of phrases that a child may say at this age. For example, a little girl might say:

'Daddy, will you marry me when I'm grown-up?' and a little boy might say:

'Mummy's mine! We're going to get married later!' When the child is going through a particularly possessive stage about one of his parents he may even talk about the 'death' of his 'rival'. For example:

'When I'm grown-up I'm going to marry Mum and I wish Dad were dead.' It should of course be remembered that the word 'death' does not mean the same thing to a child. He uses it to mean a temporary separation.

Nevertheless, this thought arises from a deep feeling for destruction and this makes the child feel guilty as he still deeply loves the parent of the same sex.

The intensity of the Oedipal stage may vary with the individual child but it never fails to cause anxiety. The young child is upset by this variety of feelings (love, preference, hostility, jealousy, worry, frustration, aggression, guilt, fear, loneliness).

It is a very delicate, but totally normal stage in his emotional development.

It only gives rise to an *Oedipus complex* if a certain number of contributory factors are present, for example: a justifiable hostility towards one of the parents because of unacceptable behaviour (an alcoholic

Fig. 3.26

father who beats the mother), the child seeing his parents making love, one parent trying to seduce the child, etc.★

Generally, if the parents have a positive attitude, the child will gradually grow out of this period of tension.

Parents must learn to understand and love him, meet his unconscious needs, teach him his place within the family and provide him with the model of a happy, well-balanced adult worthy of esteem and admiration.

The small boy wants to be big and strong like his father and the little girl wants to take after her mother. Thus imitation of the parent of the same sex plays a crucial role in ensuring a happy outcome to the Oedipal stage.

★ 'A child who has been severely punished in the course of trying to find out about sexuality is likely to grow up with a subconscious feeling of anxious guilt associated with the opposite sex.'
Mucchielli R 1974 La personnalité de l'enfant. E.S.F., Paris

REFERENCES

1 Osterrieth P 1957 L'enfant et la famille. Scarabée
2 Davidson 1960 Travail des femmes et crèches. Seminar on creches
3 Bloom B Stability and change in human characteristics. New York
4 Dossier 1970 Tout commence à la maternelle. L'éducation Feb.
5 Sommermeyer A 1975 Jouer avec les tout-petits. Editions Universitaires
6 Bernson M 1977 Du gribouillis au dessin. Delachaux et Niestle, Paris
7 Voizot B 1973 Développement de l'intelligence chez l'enfant. Colin, Paris
8 Widlocher D 1970 L'interprétation des dessins d'enfants. Dessart, Brussels
9 Luquet G H 1950 L'art primitif. Doin, Paris
10 Winnicott D W 1960 Through paediatrics to psychoanalysis. Hogarth Press, London
11 Spitz R 1963 La 1re année de la vie d l'enfant. P.U.F., Paris
12 Lelong M 1970 La propreté (Que sais-je). P.U.F., Paris
13 Freud S 3 essais sur la théorie de la sexualité. Gallimard, Paris
14 Soule M et Lebovci 1970 La connaissance de l'enfant par la psychanalyse. P.U.F., Paris
15 Freud S Outline of psychoanalysis. Hogarth Press, London

Chapter 4
Summaries

Summary of the psycho-motor development of the child from 0 to 3 years

This summary is primarily intended for students. It provides an overview of the psycho-motor development of the child taken in 2-month stages. It is therefore more easily learnt.

1st to 2nd month

	Head	*Slack*, turned to one side. The newborn can raise it from time to time (but never to an angle of more than 45° from the plane of the bed).
	Trunk	*Slack*, no muscular tone, (curvature of the back).
Postures	*Limbs*	*Hypertonicity prevails*. During the first month the child remains in the '*fetus position*' with his arms and legs tucked in.
		During the second month he becomes more supple: his abdomen lies flat and he can extend his hips.

Use of the hands

The primitive *grasp reflex*, which is very marked during the first month starts to disappear over the second month.

Sight

The newborn can follow an object through up to 90° the first month and up to 180° during the second month. Bright colours and moving objects interest him but he prefers above all the human face. He *focuses* on it attentively and might *smile* at it (during the first month it is a beatific smile; when he is 2 months old he will start to smile at people).

Hearing

The newborn reacts to loud noises (he still has the primitive Moro reflex), is interested in different sounds and is soothed by music. During the second month he can *localise* the source of sound.

Language	During the first month the baby makes *guttural sounds*. He communicates by crying and can thus indicate various kinds of discomfort. In the second month the baby starts to *vocalise* (vowel sounds using the mouth alone with no nasalisation yet).
Social development	A child of this age spends a great deal of his day eating and sleeping but he is already very *receptive* to his mother's voice and presence. He is soothed when she changes his nappy or takes him in her arms. The baby should be kept in calm surroundings without too many *stimuli* for the first 4 weeks and then should be given the stimulation of brightly coloured surroundings and his first toys (mobiles, rattles, bead counting frames).

3rd to 4th month

	Head	Held in sitting position the newborn can hold his *head upright*. Lying on his abdomen he can raise his head between 45° and 90° from the plane of the bed.
Postures	*Trunks*	*Firm back* but the lumbar region is still *weak* and still needs support (age for the baby-bouncer).
	Limbs	Hypertonicity becomes *hypotonicity*: upper and lower limbs are extended. Lying on back: the baby rolls from his back on to his sides. Lying on abdomen: the baby supports himself on his fore-arms. At 4 months he swims (flexing and extending all his limbs).

Use of the hands	The grasp reflex is replaced by *grasping on contact*. This is an involuntary reaction triggered off by contact between the object and the child's hand. He opens and closes his hand and holds the object for some moments (often taking it to his mouth). This is a tactile-motor reaction (the baby discovers through touching).
Sight	The child can turn *his head right round* to follow a moving object. He likes movement, bright colours and observes for longer periods. He discovers his hands (this is the age for *staring at the hands*) and takes them to his mouth.
Hearing	He has perfect hearing and turns his head towards the source of the sound. He can identify and accurately localise sound. He is particularly interested in the human voice.
Language	The child is very communicative and produces prolonged melodies with 'vowel sounds' and 'consonant sounds', e.g. Ah . . . roo, Ah . . . groo, etc. At this age he *gurgles* (prolonged vocalisations of combinations of syllables).
Social development	This is when the baby *starts to socialise*. He understands when his bottle is being prepared, is interested in his surroundings, gazes at everything in sight and enjoys company. To help him to take part in family life he should be put in a 'baby seat'. A child of this age uses 'body language' to make himself understood. He wriggles his whole body and moves his arms and legs when he squeals with joy or distress. He might tense his body when his mother

wants to put him to bed or lean his body in the direction of an object he covets.

Regular care is crucial at this age as babies like 'repeated actions'. They need to recognize certain gestures, certain ways of being handled (according to Anna Freud, they need to have a predictable world).

5th to 6th month

Postures	*Head and Trunk*	*Very firm.* Lying on his abdomen the infant can raise his head and trunk initially by supporting his weight on his elbows and later on his hands. From this position he can play with a toy with both hands and this is an extremely good exercise for strengthening his back muscles.
	Limbs	He is *extremely active in the use of his muscles*: 1. Held in a standing position he dances about supporting a good proportion of his own weight. This is the so-called 'skipping stage'. 2. Lying on his abdomen he becomes a plane (supporting his weight on his thorax, he raises his arms and legs) and he rolls from his abdomen on to his back. 3. Lying on his back he pedals and catches hold of his feet.

Use of the hands

Voluntary use of the hands appears: he grasps with the palm in a general, imprecise movement and will take hold of a large object set in front of him with his palm and three last fingers and takes it to his mouth (this is a tactile-visual reaction). He associates sight and touch.

Sight

The child can see perfectly from the age of 4 months and can turn round completely in both directions to follow someone.

Hearing

The child turns his head towards whoever is speaking and loves the movement of the mouth and the sound of the human voice. He is very sensitive to intonation and to music.

Language

This is the age of '*babbling*'. The child trills syllables, controls the volume, intensity and length of his utterances, monitors himself and is aware of the sounds he is making. That is why he tirelessly repeats these exercises. These are solitary games and adults should avoid interfering with them. There are other times in the day when the baby should be stimulated and given affection through speech.

Social development

At this age the infant can be introduced to a variety of foods (meat, fish, etc.) and this often causes a number of problems and so different tactics may be required to persuade the baby to eat. The atmosphere at the meal-table should always be calm and relaxed as this is the ideal time for '*socialisation*'. The child feels that he is a fully integrated member of the family and any clumsiness on his part should be overlooked (fingers in the mashed potato, overturned tumbler, etc.) as he is only trying to discover his surroundings. 6 months is also the *age for teething* and the child is often grumpy as his jaw is bothering him and he sucks any object within reach.

7th to 8th month

Postures	*Head and Trunk*	Very firm. The child can *remain sitting on his own*. He can roll over in both directions. He can lean over to pick up his toys and he can (when lying on his abdomen) raise up his entire body on his hands and feet.
	Limbs	He takes his *feet to his mouth* and sucks his big toes. He likes to play with his hands and feet (he has discovered his own body). He likes bouncing up and down when held in standing position.

Use of the hands

The child grasps an object between the thumb and little finger. He appears to make scratching or raking movements to pick up an object. He passes cubes from hand to hand and bangs them together.
He *releases* objects *voluntarily* with a movement of the *whole hand*.

Language

The is the age for *monosyllables* (da, pa, ba, ma . . .) and this constitutes the beginnings of real language. The infant should be talked to often to increase his vocabulary. He should be talked to slowly with simple words illustrated by gesture preferably during the ritual periods of the day (bathtime, when he is being dressed).

Social development

The child easily differentiates between faces. He distinguishes his mother from other people and understands that she is separate from him and can therefore leave him and this increases his anxiety. He has reached the crisis of anxiety. He cries for lengthy periods when his mother leaves him. He would like her to be there all the time and calls for her often. At this age the teddy bear becomes 'a substitute for his affections', a 'compensation'. The teddy will help him to overcome his early upsets and loneliness. The infant may also have a variety of other 'mascots' (a piece of blanket, an old nappy, etc.) which remind him of the smell of his mother and of his bed and give him a sense of security.
Parents are strongly advised not to send a child of this age to a creche (unless circumstance obliges them to do so) as he will feel 'abandoned' by his mother. At the age of 8 months the child is wary of any change in surroundings and new faces, in fact he is scared of anything 'new'.

9th to 10th month

Postures

The infant tries to *crawl* on his stomach and then progresses to '*walking on all fours*' (first on his hands and knees and then on his hands and feet).
He can *stand up on his own* by holding on to furniture but frequently falls.

Use of the hands/understanding

He can grasp small objects by the base of the thumb and the forefinger. This gives him greater independence in his use of his hands. He likes to throw objects to the ground. He learns to hand a toy to his parents: there is an exchange. He is aware of the end and the means, the container and the content. He enjoys putting objects in boxes and taking them out again; he can ring a bell and draw a ring towards him by a string.

Language

He starts to say his first words which are *'repeated syllables'* (mama, dada, byebye . . .). He understands the gist of a phrase and often makes the gesture to go with the word (waving to say goodbye). He is aware of the tone of the voice and cries if spoken to sharply. At this age a word may have many meanings as it acts as a 'symbol' (for example, milk may refer, by extension, to any liquid).

Social development

The child engages in 'feverish activity'. He cannot be still for an instant. The ability to walk on all fours enables him to discover his surroundings. He wants to touch everything in his overwhelming curiosity and this is the time when parents should study potential dangers in the home (electric wires and sockets, cleansing fluids, etc.) and make sure that they are safely out of reach.

The infant enjoys throwing objects on to the ground. He feels the need to discover the properties of everything he can touch (even the property of making a *noise* on impact with the ground). Parents are advised to be extremely patient and not to curtail their child's activities too much while keeping an eye open for any potential dangers. They should give him toys which answer his new needs and allow him freedom to move and play.

11th to 12 month

Postures

The child starts to take his first steps. The child can *walk held* first by both hands and later by one hand. He can walk by himself by holding on to furniture. He pushes chairs in front of him in his attempts to walk.

Use of the hands/understanding

The child improves his use of his thumb and forefinger to grasp. He can *release* objects with a *fine* and *precise* movement★ and enjoys throwing objects one by one (an elementary form of counting!). He starts to scribble.

He will point his forefinger at a small object and explore its third dimension (holes, cracks, grooves). He understands depth, solidity, the top and the bottom, the part and the whole, the container and the content.

He needs to *fit* objects *into* one another (to bring together two objects to form one) and likes putting baskets and boxes on his head! He practises kicking★.

Language

General meaningful language (dada byebye, milk allgone) not precise in itself but linked to specific contexts. Not all children reach this stage by one year. Language development varies from child to child between 12 and 18 months. Nonetheless, a child of this age should *understand* the meaning of a number of phrases used by his parents.

Social development

This is a *transition period* (the child uses his motor control to expand his intellectual knowledge). He has a good visual memory and notices details which often escape adults (for instance a change in the position of a piece of furniture). The child has a highly developed sense of *order* (which corresponds to a deep need for security). He likes to find objects in their right

★ This acquisition is due to control over the extensor muscles.

place. At this age he is delighted by the game of 'peekaboo' (he hides his mother's face behind a scarf and then makes it reappear to his delight, he is able to orchestrate the separation. He learns 'now it's here, now it's gone' and can still find his mother in the same place).

15th to 18th month

Postures

The child *walks by himself* at 15 months and *runs* at 18 months. At the beginning the child splays his legs to keep his balance.
At 15 months he can climb the stairs on all fours and upright with his hand held; at 21 months, he can come down the stairs with his hand held. He can kneel down unaided to pick up an object and can stand up on his own but frequently falls. He can pull an object behind him.

Use of the hands/understanding

The child enjoys *throwing, throwing back, pushing*. He can throw back a ball more efficiently. At 15 months he often falls over when he throws but at 18 months his balance has improved.
He can release an object with a fine, precise movement: he can put a button into the neck of a bottle, hold a spoon (at first he puts it into his mouth upside down). He can turn the pages of a picture book (but he skips several pages). He can point to one or two pictures, he can reproduce a line an adult has made and he scribbles. Construction: he makes towers of two to four cubes. Posting games: he can fit one plug (the round one) into the board. He can post two to three plugs at 18 months.

Language

The child improves his use of general meaningful language, for example: 'Sophy doll broken' means Sophy's doll is broken. He also orders his words according to how important they are to him and always puts himself first calling himself by his forename (or by Baby).

Social development

He is attention-seeking and likes to disrupt his mother's conversation with friends but is not yet able to cope with dialogue.
The toys which he enjoys the most are those which test his new *motor abilities*. He greatly wants to be independent but restrictions by his mother curb his initiatives. He is increasingly *sociable*: he needs adults to play with (to climb on their knees, play 'peekaboo', to take him out in his pushchair). He is also interested in group games (construction games, posting boxes, picture books) and has a longer attention span. Nonetheless, his relations with other children are not always of the best (he pinches, bites, pulls hair as if his small playmate were a toy). A child of this age prefers to play on his own with his back to other people. *His control of his bladder and bowel is irregular*, and he tends to indicate his need 'after the event!'. He likes to touch his faecal matter.

2 to 3 years

Postures

The child *runs fast* (he can turn corners). He climbs, turns, jumps, (on both feet and later on one foot). He can *climb up and down stairs by himself*. He kicks a ball (he has better balance).

Use of the hands

He can easily rotate his wrists:
He feeds himself, washes himself, opens and closes doors, puts his shoes on by himself, dresses himself, turns the pages of a picture book one by one, scribbles (at 2 years) and draws tadpole men (at 3 years).

Understanding

Good intellectual development:
He can say what four to eight pictures are (four at 2 years and eight at 3 years).
He can name four to eight common objects.
He can point to four to eight parts of his body.
He understands two to four orders given consecutively.
He can control his bladder and bowel (irregularly at 2 years, completely, both day and night, at 3 years).
Construction: he can make towers of six to eight cubes. Posting games: he can insert four shapes at 2 years and all the shapes at 3 years.
He knows two to four colours.
He can count to four at 2 years and eight at 3 years.

Language

His *vocabulary snowballs* and he uses verbs and makes explicit utterances although his language is still childish (e.g. Baby eats cake). At 2 years he always calls himself by his first name or by baby. At 3 years he uses *I* and *me* and asks many questions. He often says *no* (the age of the crisis of opposition).

Social development

2 years: crossroads

At this age the baby is half-way between being a newborn and a child. In *some ways he is mature* (he wants to be helpful and assist with certain house-hold tasks) and yet he is not independent from his mother and seems to need her more, following her everywhere and throwing tantrums.
At this age he should be closely supervised as he may often do something silly (climbing on to a window or falling down stairs). A 2-year-old child is full of contrasts: at home he can be very *bossy* (liking to give orders, wanting to do everything 'by himself', saying 'no' all the time, insisting on certain rituals). Outside, the child is shy with strangers, often finds it hard to settle at nursery school, is *not very sociable* (plays with his back to the other children, is wildly possessive about his toys, pulls hair and bites other children). *His control of bladder and bowels is irregular*. He finds it hard to get to sleep at nights (and needs certain rituals: his teddy, his doll or the door left open. He calls his mother on the slightest pretext.)

3 years: the first majority
There is an end to the excesses of the 2-year-old. The child makes progress which enables him to settle into nursery school without problems.
He is more mature: he understands what is 'allowed' and what is 'not allowed'. (he acquires a moral conscience).
He is more independent: he is not as tied to his mother.
He is more sociable: he starts to learn to wait his turn and enjoys group games (see-saws, dances, toboggans, balls) and he enjoys the company of his small playmates.
He is inquisitive: he is always asking questions and enjoys educational games (construction games, jigsaws, drawings, stories, etc.).
He is toilet trained: (night and day).
He *finds it easier to get to sleep*: if he has settled at nursery school.
He is of the age of animism and make-believe: (see pp. 96 and 98).
He asks about sex and enters the Oedipal phase: (see pp. 105 and 109).

DEVELOPMENT OF THE USE
OF THE HANDS

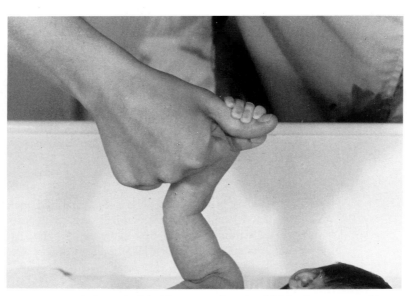

Fig. 4.1 *1st to 2nd month* Primitive *grasp* reflex: the child firmly grasps an object or a finger placed in the palm of his hand.

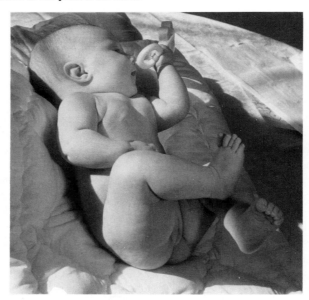

Fig. 4.2 *3rd to 4th month* *Grasping on contact* The child takes an object placed in contact with his hand and takes it to his mouth: it is an involuntary action in which sight plays no part.

Fig. 4.3 *5th to 6th month* *Voluntary palmar grasping* The infant voluntarily picks up a large object set in front of him. He picks it up with the thumb and the last three fingers of his hand. It is a general, palmar, imprecise movement. *He releases the object involuntarily.*

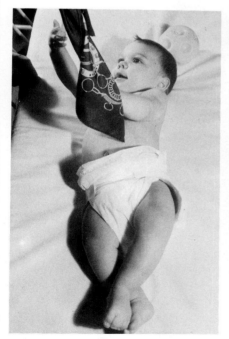

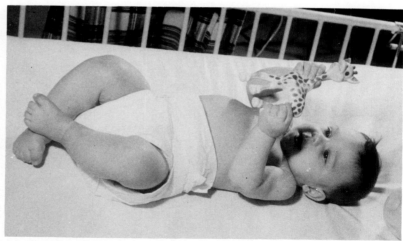

Figs 4.4 and 4.5 *7th to 8th month* *Voluntary grasping by thumb and little finger*
1. The child voluntarily picks up a large object set in front of him. He does this with his thumb and little finger.
2. *He releases the object voluntarily:* this is an imprecise, general movement.
3. He can *pass* objects from one hand to the other.
4. He *bangs* objects together on the table.

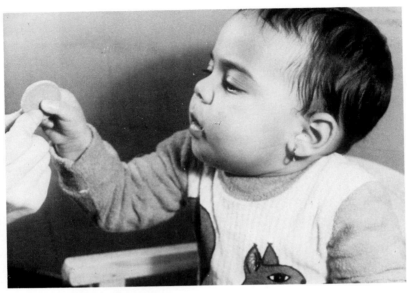

Figs 4.6 and 4.7 *9th to 10th month*
Voluntary grasping with the thumb and forefinger
The child grasps a small object between his *thumb* and *forefinger*:
— he can pull a ring by a string.
— he can ring a bell.
He *voluntarily releases* objects *with greater precision*. He enjoys throwing objects to hear the noise they make when they fall.

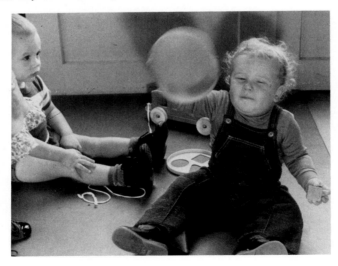

Fig. 4.8 *12th to 15th month The child can grasp and release objects with fine, precise movements.* The child starts to be manually independent and is able to feed himself, drink, colour, draw and thread objects.

DEVELOPMENT
OF SIGHT

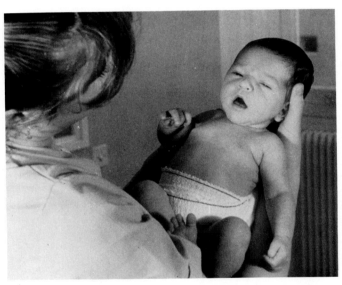

Fig. 4.9 The newborn The child *stares* at his mother's face attentively
if she is near and in front of him. He may also gaze at a source of light
in the room but he only receives a blurred image of his surroundings.

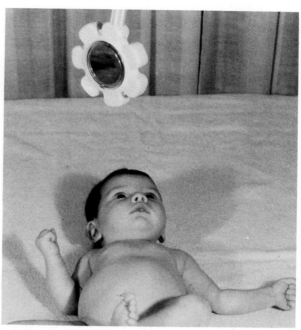

Fig. 4.10 *1 month* He can focus on a face or object in front of him and *follow* it through up to 90°.

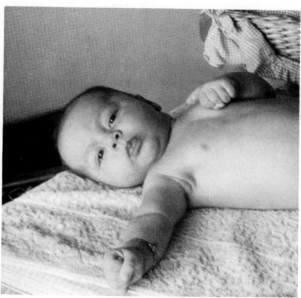

Fig. 4.11 *2 months* He can perceive, focus and adjust to distance and can *follow* a large object through up to 180° from one side of the bed to the other. When he is shown several objects he will only focus on one. He is fascinated by *bright colours*, *light* and *movement* and that is why his attention is held by a 'mobile' suspended above his head.

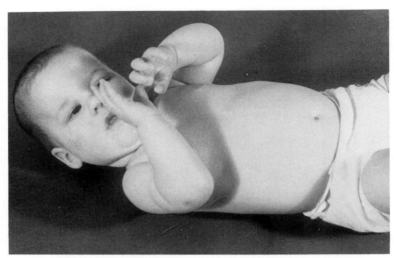

Fig. 4.12 3 months He *turns his head* right round to follow a moving object. He starts to take an interest in his body and he discovers his hands: it is the age for 'staring at his hands'. He also concentrates on nearby objects.

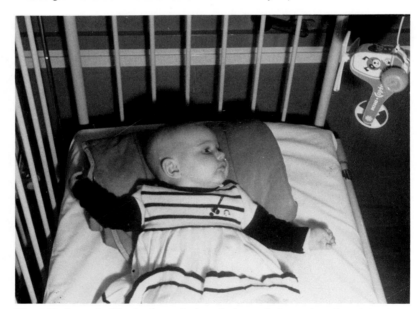

Fig. 4.13 4 months His *visual capacity is good*, almost similar to that of an adult. He can see objects at different distances and perceives small detail. From this age onwards he spends more time observing and gradually discovers his surroundings.

PSYCHO-MOTOR DEVELOPMENT

From 0 to 3 years — in cartoon strip

Postures	The newborn

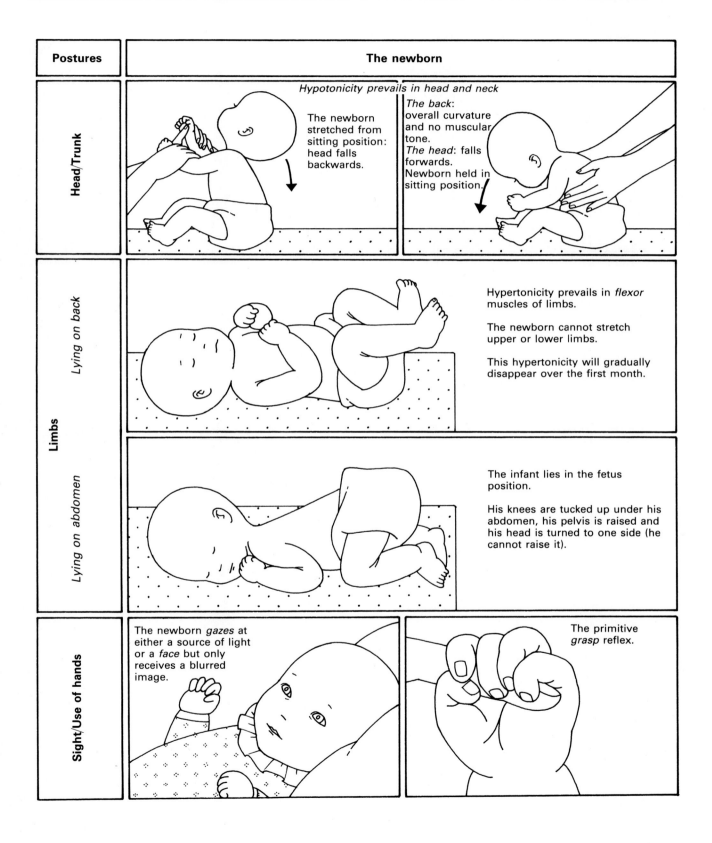

Head/Trunk

Hypotonicity prevails in head and neck

The newborn stretched from sitting position: head falls backwards.

The back: overall curvature and no muscular tone.
The head: falls forwards. Newborn held in sitting position.

Limbs

Lying on back

Hypertonicity prevails in *flexor* muscles of limbs.

The newborn cannot stretch upper or lower limbs.

This hypertonicity will gradually disappear over the first month.

Lying on abdomen

The infant lies in the fetus position.

His knees are tucked up under his abdomen, his pelvis is raised and his head is turned to one side (he cannot raise it).

Sight/Use of hands

The newborn *gazes* at either a source of light or a *face* but only receives a blurred image.

The primitive *grasp* reflex.

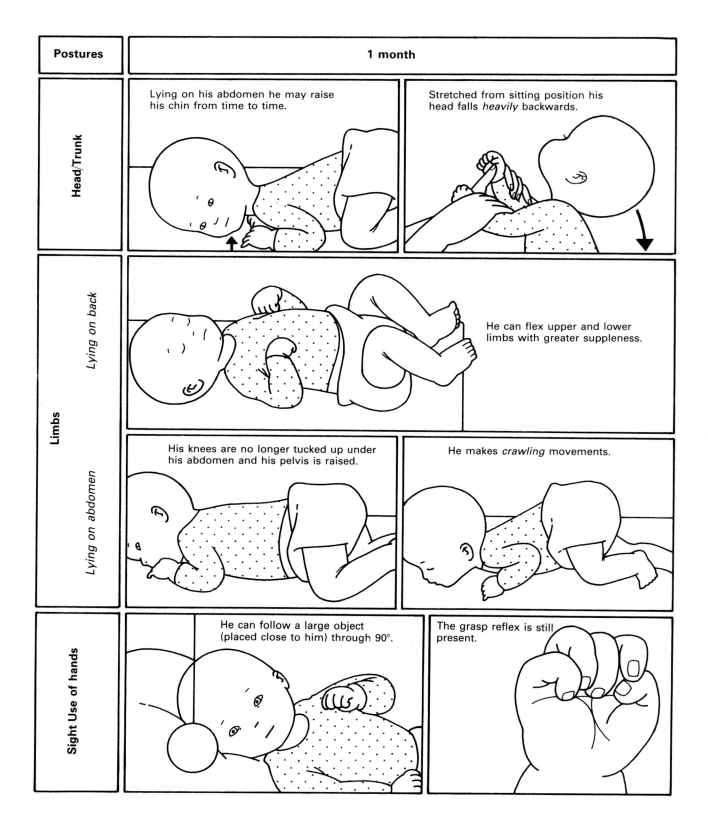

Postures	2 months	
Head/Trunk	Stretched from sitting position the head still falls backwards.	Held in sitting position the head remains upright for a few moments and *wobbles*. The back is still slack.

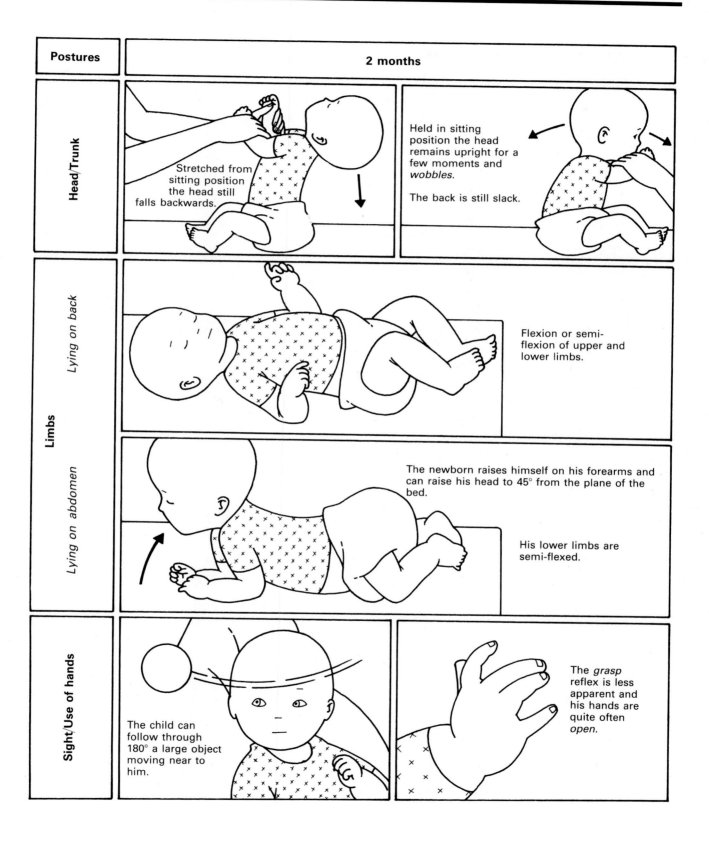

Limbs

Lying on back — Flexion or semi-flexion of upper and lower limbs.

Lying on abdomen — The newborn raises himself on his forearms and can raise his head to 45° from the plane of the bed.

His lower limbs are semi-flexed.

Sight/Use of hands

The child can follow through 180° a large object moving near to him.

The *grasp* reflex is less apparent and his hands are quite often *open*.

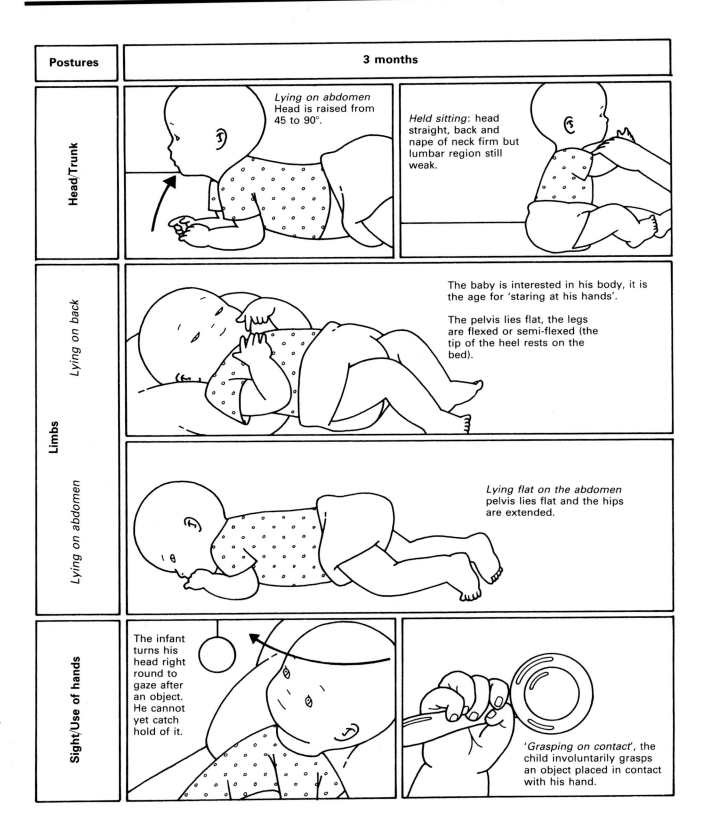

Postures	3 months

Head/Trunk

Lying on abdomen
Head is raised from 45 to 90°.

Held sitting: head straight, back and nape of neck firm but lumbar region still weak.

Limbs

Lying on back

The baby is interested in his body, it is the age for 'staring at his hands'.

The pelvis lies flat, the legs are flexed or semi-flexed (the tip of the heel rests on the bed).

Lying on abdomen

Lying flat on the abdomen pelvis lies flat and the hips are extended.

Sight/Use of hands

The infant turns his head right round to gaze after an object. He cannot yet catch hold of it.

'Grasping on contact', the child involuntarily grasps an object placed in contact with his hand.

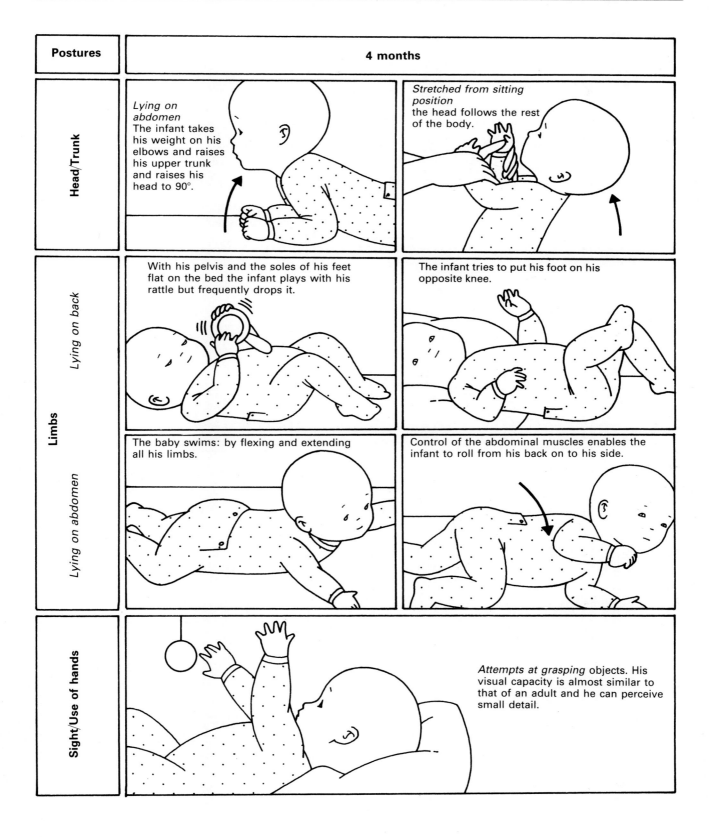

Postures	4 months

Head/Trunk

Lying on abdomen
The infant takes his weight on his elbows and raises his upper trunk and raises his head to 90°.

Stretched from sitting position
the head follows the rest of the body.

Limbs

Lying on back

With his pelvis and the soles of his feet flat on the bed the infant plays with his rattle but frequently drops it.

The infant tries to put his foot on his opposite knee.

Lying on abdomen

The baby swims: by flexing and extending all his limbs.

Control of the abdominal muscles enables the infant to roll from his back on to his side.

Sight/Use of hands

Attempts at grasping objects. His visual capacity is almost similar to that of an adult and he can perceive small detail.

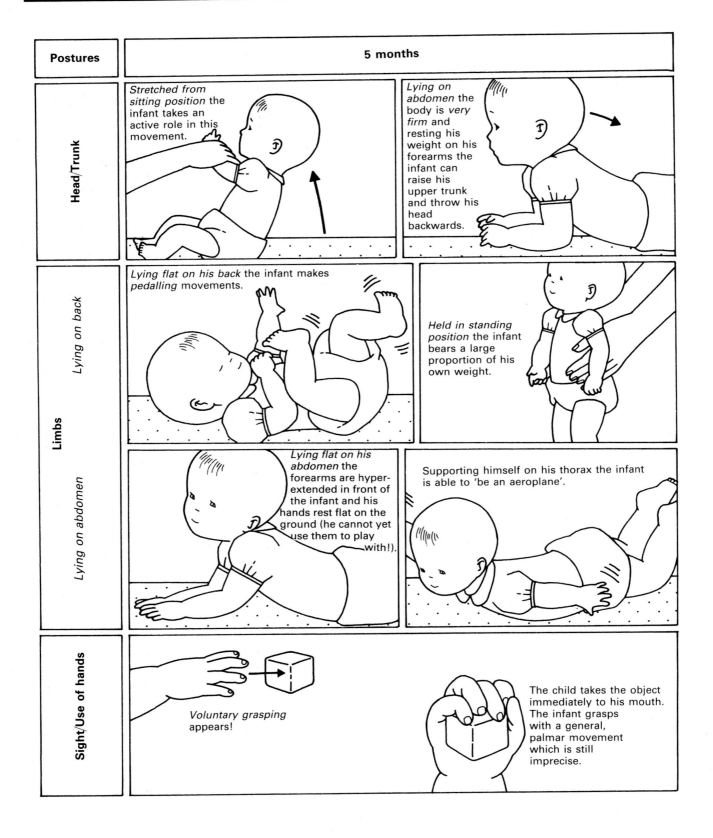

Postures	5 months	
Head/Trunk	*Stretched from sitting position* the infant takes an active role in this movement.	*Lying on abdomen* the body is *very firm* and resting his weight on his forearms the infant can raise his upper trunk and throw his head backwards.
Limbs — *Lying on back*	*Lying flat on his back* the infant makes *pedalling* movements.	*Held in standing position* the infant bears a large proportion of his own weight.
Lying on abdomen	*Lying flat on his abdomen* the forearms are hyper-extended in front of the infant and his hands rest flat on the ground (he cannot yet use them to play with!).	Supporting himself on his thorax the infant is able to 'be an aeroplane'.
Sight/Use of hands	*Voluntary grasping* appears!	The child takes the object immediately to his mouth. The infant grasps with a general, palmar movement which is still imprecise.

Postures	6 months

Head/Trunk

Lying on abdomen the child can raise himself up on his hands

Lying on his back the child can raise his head and shoulders from the plane of the bed.

Limbs

Lying on back

Lying flat on his back the infant likes playing with his feet.

Held in a standing position the child is in what is called the 'skipping' stage (he jumps up and crouches down on his legs).

Lying on abdomen

Lying flat on his abdomen the infant can easily play with his hands.

He can roll from his abdomen on to his back.

Sight/Use of hands

The child has acquired the capacity for general, voluntary grasping.

He can hold two cubes in his hands but if he drops them he does not look for them.

Postures	7 months

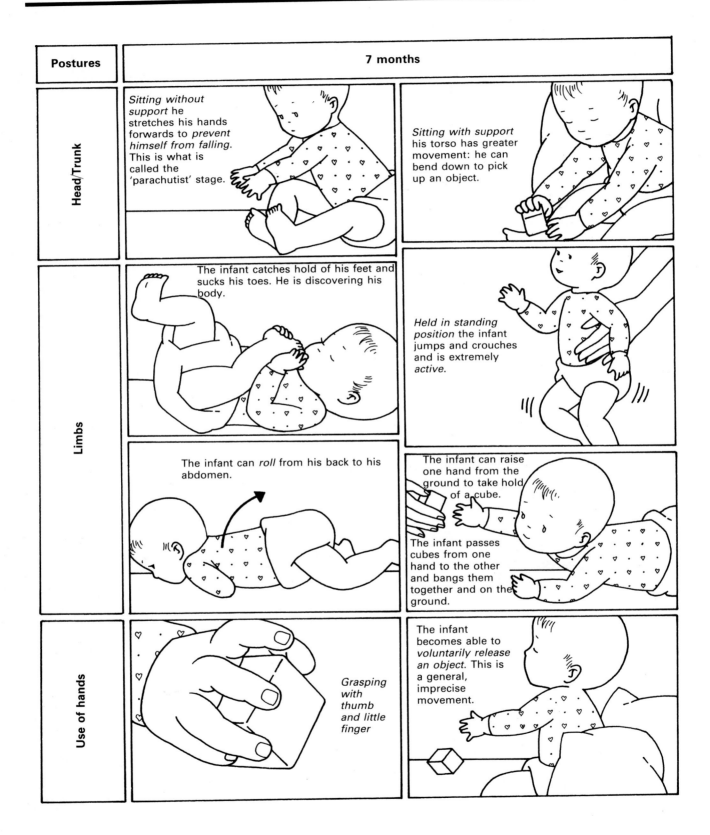

Sitting without support he stretches his hands forwards to *prevent himself from falling.* This is what is called the 'parachutist' stage.

Sitting with support his torso has greater movement: he can bend down to pick up an object.

Head/Trunk

The infant catches hold of his feet and sucks his toes. He is discovering his body.

Held in standing position the infant jumps and crouches and is extremely *active.*

Limbs

The infant can *roll* from his back to his abdomen.

The infant can raise one hand from the ground to take hold of a cube.

The infant passes cubes from one hand to the other and bangs them together and on the ground.

Use of hands

Grasping with thumb and little finger

The infant becomes able to *voluntarily release an object.* This is a general, imprecise movement.

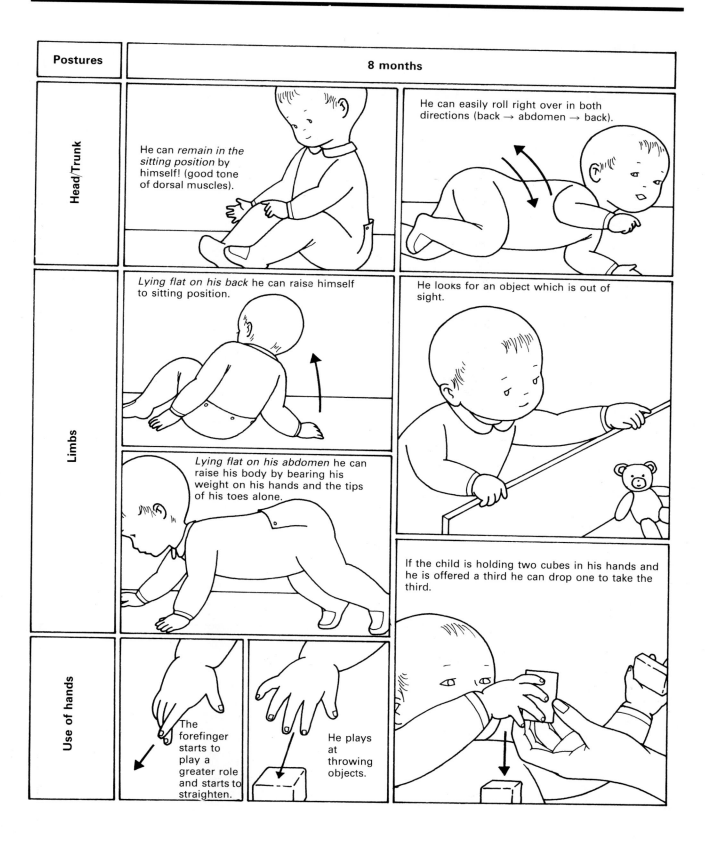

Postures	8 months

Head/Trunk

He can *remain in the sitting position* by himself! (good tone of dorsal muscles).

He can easily roll right over in both directions (back → abdomen → back).

Limbs

Lying flat on his back he can raise himself to sitting position.

Lying flat on his abdomen he can raise his body by bearing his weight on his hands and the tips of his toes alone.

He looks for an object which is out of sight.

If the child is holding two cubes in his hands and he is offered a third he can drop one to take the third.

Use of hands

The forefinger starts to play a greater role and starts to straighten.

He plays at throwing objects.

	9 months
Postures	He learns to *crawl* (he starts by going backwards)! He stands up by holding on to furniture or his playpen, remains standing for a few moments and then falls.
Use of hands/Understanding	*Grasping with thumb and forefinger*: he can grasp a small object between the base of the thumb and the forefinger. He draws a thread by a string. He learns to hand a toy to his parents.

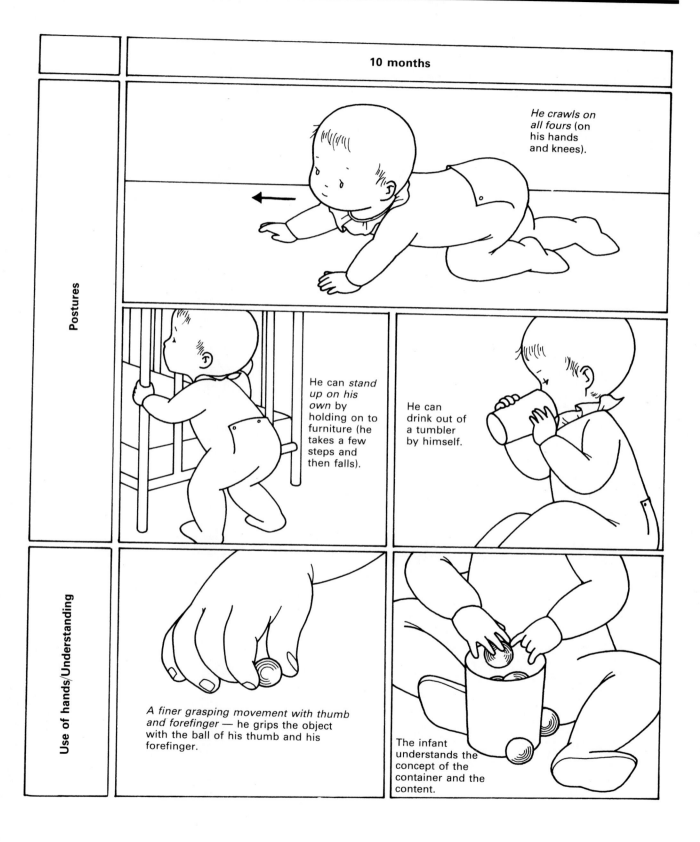

10 months

Postures

He crawls on all fours (on his hands and knees).

He can *stand up on his own* by holding on to furniture (he takes a few steps and then falls).

He can drink out of a tumbler by himself.

Use of hands/Understanding

A finer grasping movement with thumb and forefinger — he grips the object with the ball of his thumb and his forefinger.

The infant understands the concept of the container and the content.

11 months

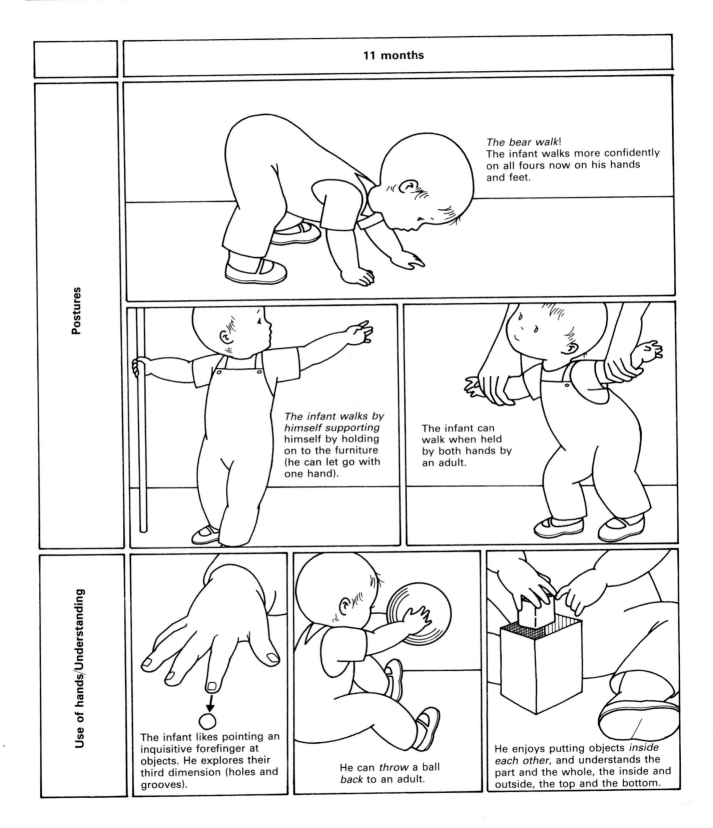

Postures

The bear walk!
The infant walks more confidently on all fours now on his hands and feet.

The infant walks by himself supporting himself by holding on to the furniture (he can let go with one hand).

The infant can walk when held by both hands by an adult.

Use of hands/Understanding

The infant likes pointing an inquisitive forefinger at objects. He explores their third dimension (holes and grooves).

He can *throw* a ball *back* to an adult.

He enjoys putting objects *inside each other*, and understands the part and the whole, the inside and outside, the top and the bottom.

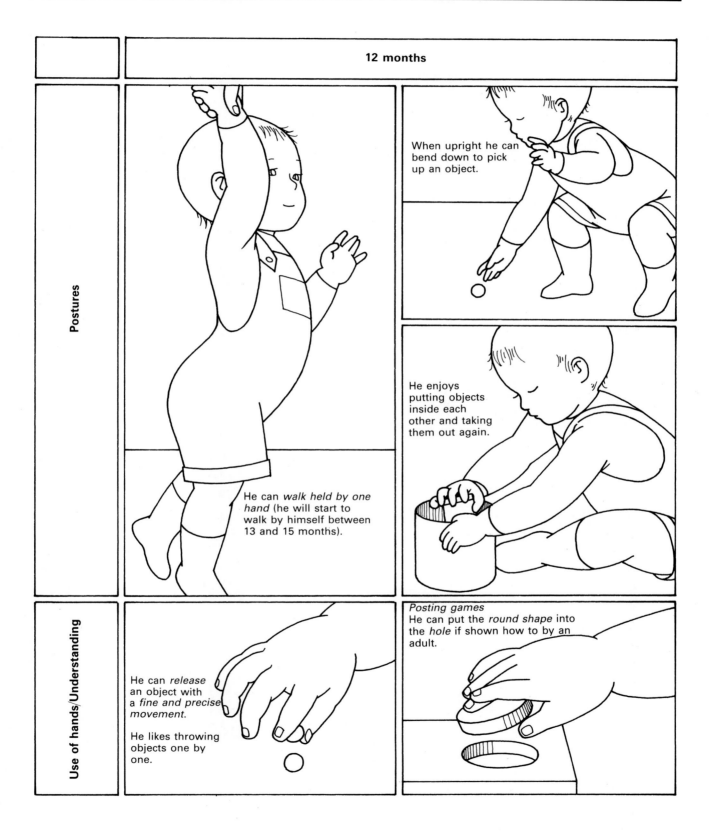

12 months

Postures

He can *walk held by one hand* (he will start to walk by himself between 13 and 15 months).

When upright he can bend down to pick up an object.

He enjoys putting objects inside each other and taking them out again.

Use of hands/Understanding

He can *release* an object with a *fine and precise movement*.

He likes throwing objects one by one.

Posting games
He can put the *round shape* into the *hole* if shown how to by an adult.

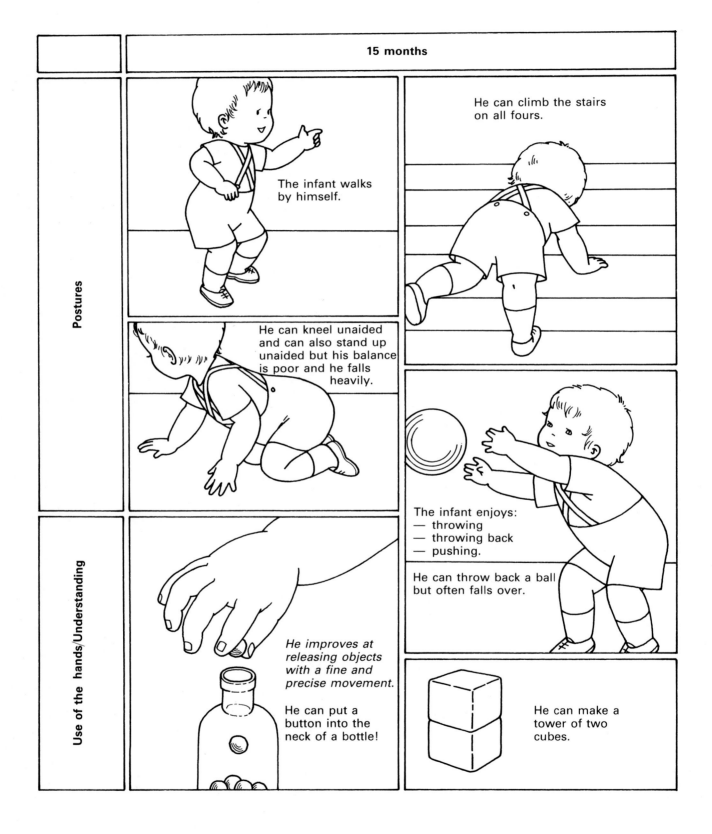

15 months

Postures

The infant walks by himself.

He can climb the stairs on all fours.

He can kneel unaided and can also stand up unaided but his balance is poor and he falls heavily.

The infant enjoys:
— throwing
— throwing back
— pushing.

He can throw back a ball but often falls over.

Use of the hands/Understanding

He improves at releasing objects with a fine and precise movement.

He can put a button into the neck of a bottle!

He can make a tower of two cubes.

15 months

Drawing
The infant can *reproduce* a *line* made by an adult.

Use of hands/Understanding

He can hold a spoon (but puts it into his mouth upside down).

He can turn the pages of his picture (but he *skips* several pages at a time!).

18 months

He can climb up and down stairs with his hand held.

He can crouch down to pick up an object.

He can *pull* a toy behind him while he is walking.

He runs (arms and legs apart) and falls very frequently.

He can make towers of three cubes.

He can *push* a ball with his foot without falling.

2 years

The infant can go up and down stairs unaided.

The infant jumps on both feet or even dances.

The infant climbs.

He tries to *wash* his face and dry it *by himself.*

Drawing: this is the age for 'scribbling'.

He can feed himself without making a mess.

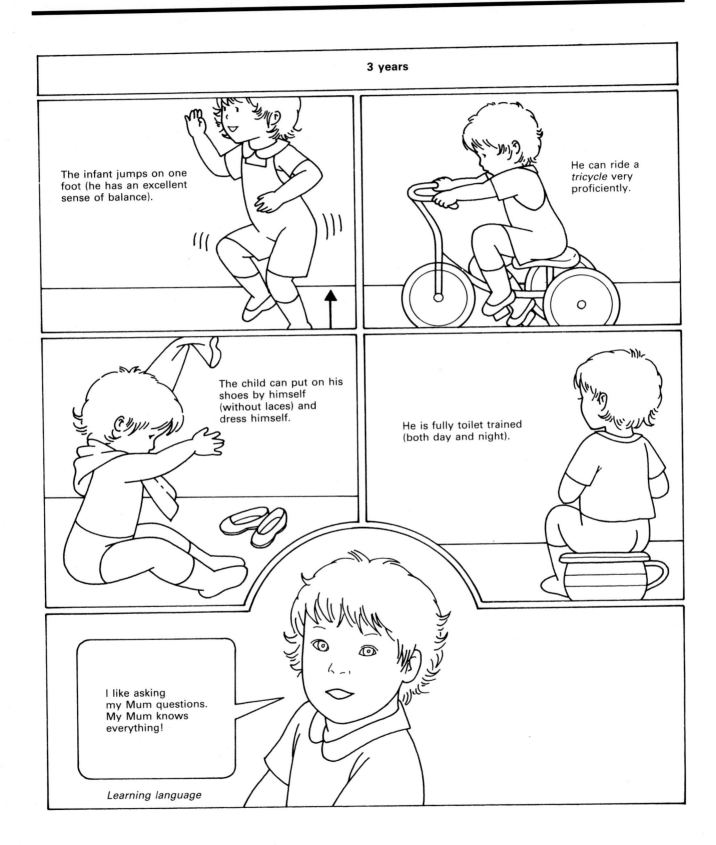

3 years

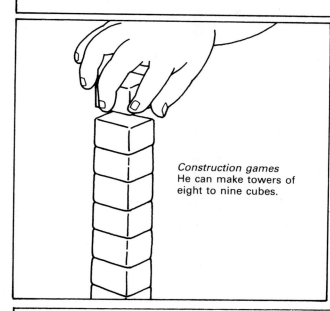

Construction games
He can make towers of eight to nine cubes.

Posting games
He can slot *all the shapes* into the board.

The child can count to six or eight.

He can *point to*:
— six to eight common objects.
— six to eight parts of his body.
— six to eight pictures.

He knows three to four *colours*.

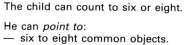

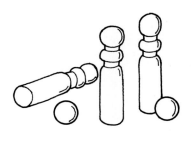

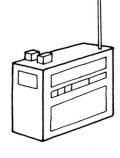

FURTHER READING

Bruner J, Cole M, Lloyd B (eds) 1977 The developing child. (Series: Mothering — Rudolph Schaffer: Play — Catherine Garvey: Distress and comfort — Judy Dunn; The perceptual world of the child — Tom Bower; Children's drawings — Jacqueline Goodnow; The first relationship — Daniel Stern.) Fontana/Open Books, London

Freud S 1977 On sexuality. (ed. A. Richards). Penguin, Harmondsworth

Gesell A 1971 First five years of life: a guide to the study of the pre-school child. Methuen, London

Gessell A, Ilg F L 1975 Infant and child in the culture of today. Hamilton, London

Illingworth R S, Illingworth C M 1977 Babies and young children. A guide for parents, 6th edn. Churchill Livingstone, Edinburgh

Illingworth R S 1980 The development of the infant and young child. Abnormal and normal, 7th edn. Churchill Livingstone, Edinburgh

Sheridan M D 1976 Children's developmental progress from birth to five (Stycar series) NFER Publishing. Windsor, Berks

Open University 1977 The first years of life. Ward Lock, London

Feeding
Health Visitors' Association 1979 Feeding children in the first year. Edsall, London

Play
Jeffree D M, McConky R, Hewson S 1979 Let me play. Allen & Unwin, London

Newson J, Newson E 1979 Toys and playthings. Allen & Unwin, London.

Child rearing, parenting, social aspects
Pringle M K 1980 A fairer future for children. (National Children's Bureau series) Macmillan, London

Also recommended
Clarke A M, Clarke A D B (eds) 1976 Early experience: myth and evidence. Open Books, London — presents psychology and recent theories in more depth

Mother and newborn 1981 Part 2 Nursing (add-on journal) 1st series, no. 22 — available in nursing department libraries

Index